Weather To Travel

Presented by Maria Harding

'Whether the weather be cold
Or whether the weather be hot
We'll weather the weather
Whatever the weather
Whether we like it or not'

(anon)

Contents

Acknowledgements

The weather statistics have been included by courtesy of the Meteorological Office. We are also indebted to C G Smith, co-author with E A Pearce of The World Weather Guide, for his invaluable contribution of climatic information for the individual country weather profiles.

Weather To Travel

Presented by: Maria Harding

Editor: Amanda Parry
Deputy Editor: Debbie Metherell
Consultant on Climate: C G Smith
Researched by: William Blackwell
Illustrated by: Mike Peyton
Cover Design: Switch, Birmingham
Text Design & Layout: Zai Khan
Maps by: Oxford Cartographers

This edition edited and designed by:

Tomorrow's Guides
6 Alleyn Road, London SE21 8AL

Tel: 0181-766 6540
Fax: 0181-766 7029

Typeset and printed in Great Britain

First published 1996
Millennium edition 1998

© **Tomorrow's Guides Ltd 1998**

ISBN 1 85890 012 3

All rights reserved. No part of this work may be reproduced or utilised in any form by any means, electronic or mechanical, including photocopying, recording or by any information storage and retrieval system, without the prior written permission of the publishers.

A CIP catalogue record for this book is available from the British Library.

The publishers would appreciate any information that will assist them in keeping future editions up to date. Although all reasonable care has been taken in the preparation of this book, neither the publishers, the author, PowerGen or companies/organisations associated with this book can accept any liability for any consequences arising from the use of the information contained within this book.

Introduction by Maria Harding

Weather To Travel provides a country-by-country review of the world's weather, guiding you through local seasons and advising you on what clothes to take, when best to go, and when you should definitely stay away. Obviously, it is impossible to say exactly what the weather will be like in any particular country or area on a specific day, but this book will tell you what weather can be anticipated during a particular season, based on historical climatic data.

It also provides you with our own month by month `comfort rating' for your chosen destination. This takes into account temperature and humidity levels and is designed to give you an indication of how comfortable (or uncomfortable) you will feel in a particular region at a specific time of year. Often in hot climates the sticky conditions caused by heat and high humidity are tempered by sea breezes or local winds, but since these vary greatly from day to day our comfort rating presents you with the `worst case scenario' - telling you how you will feel in a particular location on a windless day.

For an at-a-glance idea of the climate which prevails in your chosen destination - maritime, continental, tropical, subtropical, Mediterranean and so on - see the climate maps provided for each country, and the World Climate Map and descriptions. These will give you an idea of the general conditions which dictate the local weather and help you quickly to prepare a checklist of essential items - an obvious example is that sun glasses and protective cream are a must for tropical, subtropical and desert climates.

You will find detailed instructions on how to use this book set out on the next two pages. These include a section with advice on what to pack. Health immunisation requirements/ recommendations are not included within the book and you should check these with your GP or with current Department of Health guidelines.

In compiling *Weather To Travel,* we have taken no account of the political regimes which prevail in different parts of the world - the weather is the weather, regardless of what human beings get up to. However, before you embark on a journey to a country with a regime unsympathetic to human rights, we would advise you to consult your travel agent or check with the Foreign Office for an update on local conditions and advice on safety.

Write to: *Travel Advice Unit, Consular Division, Foreign and Commonwealth Office, 1 Palace Street, London SW1E 5HE or telephone 0171-238 4503/4, Fax: 0171-238 4545*

Finding a Country/Destination

Wherever in the world you're planning to visit, you'll find its climate and local weather conditions reviewed within this book, together with advice on what to pack and when - ideally - to go. For quick access to this information, we have listed countries in alphabetical order. Look at the top of pages 8 to 91 to locate the country you are interested in, or turn to the weather statistics tables at the back.

World Climate

On pages 6 and 7 you will find a colour-coded world map giving an at-a-glance guide to climates found in each area of the world. There is also an explanation for each of the 12 different climatic types (eg Tropical Equatorial, Continental) which together make up the World's climate and dictate the weather pattern for a particular country or region.

Country Weather Profiles

There are individual weather profiles for 205 countries worldwide set out on pages 8 to 91 where, in addition, you will find country climate maps, at-a-glance monthly rainfall, comfort and sunshine hours statistics, together with advice on what to pack and when to visit. In large land masses such as America, Russia and India, climatic conditions vary from region to region. Where this is the case, we profile weather region by region.

The weather profiles also highlight the effects of wind chill factor on winter temperatures and of local winds on summer humidity levels. Attention is drawn to known problem areas such as countries with a seasonal risk of hurricanes (eg the Caribbean), and warnings are given where there is a known danger like that of heat stroke.

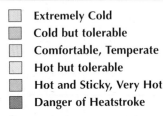

While it is impossible to state exactly what the weather will be like during any particular day or week, long term assessment of seasonal conditions provides a clear weather pattern which has been historically established as that which is most likely to prevail at a specific time of year - short of freak developments like that which brought Britain's 'hurricane' in October 1987.

Comfort *(It's not the heat, it's the humidity)* Adjacent to the weather profiles, you will find month-by-month details of your chosen destination's `comfort rating' - an indication of just how cold or, conversely, how hot and humid this particular region can get. We have colour coded a range of conditions for an at-at-glance guide - the colour codes denote:

- **Extremely Cold**
- **Cold but tolerable**
- **Comfortable, Temperate**
- **Hot but tolerable**
- **Hot and Sticky, Very Hot**
- **Danger of Heatstroke**

You should take account of your age and physical condition when trying to assess how badly you could be affected by high humidity. For example, those with heart and chest conditions could feel discomfort at times when others have no problem. In cold climates, the cooling power of the wind (wind chill) makes one feel even colder.

World and Country Maps

On pages 92 and 93 you will find a World Map showing all the countries and destinations featured within this book. The letters across the top of this map combined with the numbers down the side provide the key to the `World Map Reference' included at the start of each weather profile, where we also state whether a country is within the southern hemisphere. For these countries references to `summer' within the profiles are to the equivalent months of our winter, and vice versa.

The small country maps to the right of each weather profile show the respective country colour-coded according to its climatic type/s, and the names of locations featured within the Weather Statistics. The maps also show neighbouring countries.

Weather Statistics

You will find month-by-month tables on pages 94 to 103 which detail 315 locations around the world in terms of their monthly average rainfall, daily hours of sunshine, maximum/minimum temperatures and midday humidity. All statistics are based on records kept at local weather stations compiled over periods from 5 to 75 years.

Rainfall (or precipitation) includes all forms of moisture falling to ground during that month (mainly rain or snow) and is expressed in millimetres. At the foot of each left hand page there is a conversion scale from millimetres to inches. Approximately 25 millimetres equal 1 inch.

Sunshine - the number of hours is based on the daily hours of bright sunshine averaged over the entire month.

Temperatures - the average monthly temperatures in the tables are expressed in degrees Centigrade (Fahrenheit temperatures are also given in the weather profiles). If you are more familiar with the Fahrenheit system than with Centigrade, you can easily convert temperatures. Multiply the Centigrade figure by 9, divide by 5 and add 32; for example, 15 degrees Centigrade is 59 degrees Fahrenheit. At the foot of each right hand page of the tables there is a conversion scale from Centigrade to Fahrenheit.

Relative Humidity is expressed as a percentage and the value shown represents that of the hottest time of day, usually between 12 noon and 2 p.m. A relative humidity of 100% means that the moisture content of the air is the maximum possible at that particular temperature.

Abbreviations, Terms
We have used the following abbreviations throughout this book:

°C	**Degrees Centigrade**
°F	**Degrees Fahrenheit**
ft	**Feet**
in	**Inches**
m	**Metres**
mm	**Millimetres**

At the very back of the book we have included a Glossary with descriptions of the Wind Names and other climatic terms (such as Wind Chill Factor) used within the Weather Profiles.

What to Pack
By consulting this book before you start packing, you can save yourself the sweat of lugging along baggage you won't need - and the inconvenience of leaving behind gear that you will. Each country's profile will guide you on the type of clothing you will need (highlighted by ▥) but there are a few additional points worth considering when you draw up your checklist of essentials:-

● Always take a warm cover-up, even if visiting a very hot country. It will be useful on a chilly night flight and will also counter the effects of indoor air conditioning, as well as coming in handy if you encounter cool weather on your return.

● Buy easily washable, crease-resistant clothing that can be rinsed through and worn again and again. Anything with Lycra is a good bet, while garments made from a mix of man made and natural fibres will crease less than pure cotton or linen outfits.

● If visiting a country with a cold climate, invest in good quality thermals and remember that many layers of light clothes will keep you warmer, and more comfortable, than a few heavy items.

● Keep the thin plastic bags dry cleaners use to wrap clothes in - they're invaluable for keeping creases at bay when packing.

● If you're desperate to appear crumple-free after a long flight, remember the old trick of hanging clothes over a steamy bath. It does work.

● If you travel frequently, buy a duplicate toilet bag and stock it with miniature versions of toiletries. Keep essentials like travel hairdryers, irons, adaptors, sunglasses and even clean underwear permanently packed to cut preparation time.

● If you are on a course of medication, remember to pack a good supply - it will be at best expensive and at worst unobtainable once you're on the hoof.

● Suncreams should not be kept from one trip to the next - throw them out after two months. After this, sunscreens can lose their effectiveness and you could inadvertently burn yourself.

● Invest in a wheeled suitcase - and don't fill it to overflowing; you may need some space for bargains you buy abroad. Remember that experienced travellers always travel light, so plan a co-ordinated lightweight travel wardrobe that you can mix and match ad infinitum, and never exceed one suitcase if you can possibly help it.

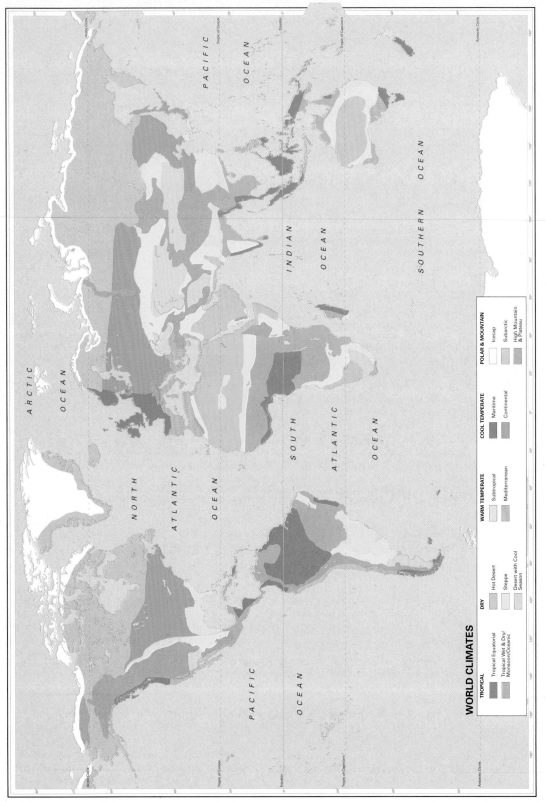

WORLD CLIMATES

TROPICAL

Tropical Equatorial

Tropical Wet & Dry/
Monsoon/Oceanic

DRY

Hot Desert

Steppe

Desert with Cool
Season

WARM TEMPERATE

Subtropical

Mediterranean

COOL TEMPERATE

Maritime

Continental

POLAR & MOUNTAIN

Icecap

Subarctic

High Mountain
& Plateau

World Climates have been summarised below under 12 climatic types each distinguished by its own colour, and illustrated on the World Map opposite. The smaller more detailed country maps on pages 8 to 91 use the same colour coding to denote the climatic types applicable to each country.

Tropical Climates

Tropical Equatorial
Also known as *Tropical Rainforest,* found approximately 5° north or south of the equator where there is no real dry season and rain can and does occur year round. These climates produce hot and sticky conditions.

Tropical Wet & Dry/Monsoon/Oceanic
Occurring between roughly 5° and 20° north and south of the equator, these climates have a distinct dry season contrasting with the wet season which occurs generally at the time of high sun. They include *Tropical Monsoon* climates found mainly in southern Asia, *Savanna* (open grasslands) characteristic of much of tropical Africa and *Tropical Oceanic* climates found in the Caribbean.

Dry Climates

Hot Desert
The true hot desert climates with very high day time temperatures, little rain all year and no real cool season, although temperatures may drop sharply at night. The best examples are the Sahara desert, the deserts of the Middle East and central Australia.

Steppe or Semi-Desert
The climates of tropical grasslands and the semi-arid edges of hot deserts where there is usually some rain occurring in one season of the year. Examples are the Sahel region of Africa and the central drier regions of India.

Desert with Cool Season
Also known as *Cold Desert* climates, which occur at higher latitudes in the interior of continents such as the Gobi desert in Mongolia. They are in effect continental climates with considerable extremes of temperature - the winter season is cold to very cold but summers are often warm to hot.

Warm Temperate Climates

Temperate Climates differ from Tropical Climates in that they have a definite cool season

Subtropical
Summer is the wettest but also the hottest time of year, winters are mild with occasional cold spells and some rain. These climates are found in the southeast of United States and in parts of South America, South Africa, China and Australia.

Mediterranean
Summers are hot and dry, winters are mild but have disturbed weather conditions and nearly all the annual rainfall. These climates are called *Mediterranean* as they are found extensively around the Mediterranean Sea, but also occur in smaller but important areas of California, central Chile, the Cape region of South Africa, and Western/South Australia.

Cool Temperate Climates

These are found on the poleward sides of warm temperate climates

Maritime
Also called *Oceanic* climates, which have a small range of temperature variation so winters are mild to cool, rarely very cold and summers not particularly hot; rain occurs in all seasons. They are found in Great Britain and northwest Europe, British Columbia and the northwest coast of United States, Southern Chile, Tasmania and New Zealand.

Continental
These climates have a warm to hot summer and a cold winter, with some rain in all seasons. Winters vary from being severe to rather less cold conditions. They occur in the centre and the east of each of North America, Europe and Asia.

Polar & Mountain Climates

Icecap
Also known as *Arctic* climates, all months have an average temperature of below 0°C (32°F). The most extensive areas are Antarctica (South Pole), and central Greenland; also the coastline of Northern Russia and islands within the Arctic and Antarctic circles, such as Spitzbergen and South Georgia. (The North Pole lies at the centre of the Arctic Ocean).

Subarctic
Winters are long and very cold, but during the short summer season temperatures can rise surprisingly high, so that snow melts completely for a period. These climates occur in central and northern Canada, and northern Russia. Also known as *Tundra* - a treeless zone lying between the icecap and the timberline of North America and Eurasia - and *Taiga* - coniferous forests stretching across the lower part of subarctic North America and Eurasia.

High Mountain & Plateau
Climates of areas of mountain and plateau above the tree line containing permanent snow cover. They are found primarily in the mountain ranges of North and South America, the Alpine regions and the Himalayas and Tibet.

Afghanistan

Capital City: **Kabul** World Map ref: **G3**

Afghanistan is a largely mountainous country and, in its higher reaches, wintry conditions prevail throughout the year. On the lower ground of its southwest and northwest borders, summers are very sunny, hot and dry with extremely high temperatures; along its southwest border with Iran, the heat is exacerbated by dusty desert winds. Winters are severe with substantial rainfall from December to March. In the mountains, summers are sunny and warm, winters are harsh and the heaviest rainfall comes in spring.
■ Pack carefully for a trip to Afghanistan: light summer clothing should include head covers to protect against heat and dust. In the winter, take very warm clothes and hats. Women should respect the Islamic dress code.

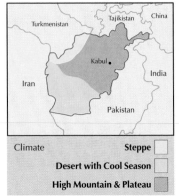

Kabul
Alt: 1,815m (6,000ft)

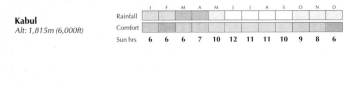

	J	F	M	A	M	J	J	A	S	O	N	D
Rainfall												
Comfort												
Sun hrs	6	6	6	7	10	12	11	11	10	9	8	6

Climate   **Steppe** ☐

Desert with Cool Season ☐

High Mountain & Plateau ■

Albania

Capital City: **Tirana** World Map ref: **F2**

Albania has a mixture of climates. Its Mediterranean coast enjoys mainly dry, sunny summers and mild, rainy winters while its mountainous interior is cool. In the autumn a warmer wind, the Sirocco, arrives bringing with it high humidity and sticky, muggy weather. ■ Pack light clothing for a summer visit supplemented by warmer wear if you are planning a trip to the mountains. Warm clothing and rainwear is de rigeur in the winter and thermals are a good idea for the mountains.

Tirana
Alt: 90m (300ft)

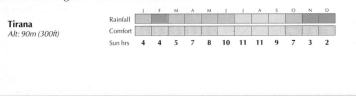

	J	F	M	A	M	J	J	A	S	O	N	D
Rainfall												
Comfort												
Sun hrs	4	4	5	7	8	10	11	11	9	7	3	2

Climate   **Mediterranean** ■

Continental ■

Algeria

Capital City: **Algiers** World Map ref: **E3**

With the Western Sahara Desert covering over 80% of the country, Algeria is hot, hot, hot, particularly in the south and especially during its long summer. Expect the unexpected here: sandstorms can be a flight-delaying nuisance in the south during the arid summer months, while the country's coastal towns pay for the sea breezes they bask in by attracting the occasional fierce storm. Southern Algeria comes into its own in the winter months when its oases attract hordes of sun worshippers. Rain in this region is very rare; indeed, Algeria, as a whole, has a low level of rainfall. ■ Take plenty of light cotton clothes but in winter be prepared to layer up for cold nights in the Sahara and the Atlas mountains. Nights are warmer on the coast.

Algiers
Alt: 60m (200ft)

	J	F	M	A	M	J	J	A	S	O	N	D
Rainfall												
Comfort												
Sun hrs	5	6	7	7	8	9	10	10	8	6	5	4

Climate   **Hot Desert** ☐   **Steppe** ☐

Mediterranean ■

   Monthly Rainfall

mm		5		25		75		150		300+
in		0.2		1		3		6		12+

Andorra

Capital City: **Andorra La Vella** World Map ref: **E2**

This lovely little principality, which nestles among the eastern Pyrenees, is popular with skiers because its snowy slopes are bright, sunny and crisp in the winter months. Andorra is equally enjoyable in the summer when the climate is mainly dry, fresh and sunny but not really hot enough to suit those who relish shirtsleeve weather.  Supplement light clothing with warmer cover-ups in the summer months, especially for the evenings. Brace yourself for frost and snow in the winter.

Andorra La Vella
Alt: 1,080m (3,500ft)

	J	F	M	A	M	J	J	A	S	O	N	D
Rainfall												
Comfort												
Sun hrs	4	5	6	6	7	7	9	8	7	5	5	4

Climate   **High Mountain & Plateau**

Angola

Capital City: **Luanda** World Map ref: **F5** (In southern hemisphere)

Angola, which has a narrow coastal plain and a range of inland plateau, has a healthy and pleasant climate for a tropical country. It has one wet season from October to April and rainfall is heaviest on higher ground. On the coast, a cold oceanic current brings much fog and cloud as well as sea breezes which moderate temperatures but bring little rain. Inland temperatures are reduced by altitude. 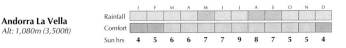 Recommendations on clothing vary according to the area of Angola being visited: light clothes are fine but, if travelling inland, be prepared for chilly weather, especially at night, and take waterproofs during the rainy season.

Luanda
Alt: 45m (150ft)

	J	F	M	A	M	J	J	A	S	O	N	D
Rainfall												
Comfort												
Sun hrs	7	7	7	6	7	7	5	5	5	5	6	6

Climate   **Tropical Wet & Dry**
Steppe

Anguilla

Capital City: **The Valley** World Map ref: **C4**

Anguilla lies in the middle of the Leeward Islands and, as well as being big on tourism, it is famous for its lobsters and is a major exporter of salt. It has a tropical oceanic climate which produces some rain all year. The wettest months are from May to December and, between July and November, you could encounter hurricane conditions. Typically for a Caribbean island, Anguilla's summer is hotter than the winter but temperatures are never extreme, averaging 27°C (80°F) throughout the year. Even at its hottest, the island is never unbearable because sea breezes help dissipate the humidity, although it can feel sticky at night.  Pack light cotton clothing with cover-ups for the occasional chilly winter evening and be prepared for rain if you are visiting during the summer months.

The Valley
Alt: 30m (100ft)

	J	F	M	A	M	J	J	A	S	O	N	D
Rainfall												
Comfort												
Sun hrs	8	8	9	9	9	9	9	9	8	8	8	8

Climate   **Tropical Oceanic**

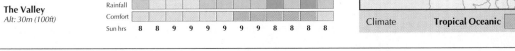

Cold but tolerable	Hot but tolerable	Danger of Heatstroke
Extremely Cold	Comfortable, Temperate	Hot & Sticky, Very Hot

Key to Comfort

Antigua

Capital City: **St John's**   World Map ref: **C4**

Antigua is the largest of the Leeward Islands and its inhabitants are heavily into tourism and cricket. Its "sister" island, Barbuda, is a complete contrast: very exclusive with just two luxury hotels and a frigate colony. Torrential rain and the occasional hurricane can afflict these islands between July and November but, outside the rainy season, the islands are dryer than many parts of the Caribbean. They are consistently hot with an all year average of 8-9 hours of sunshine a day. Winters are slightly cooler. The heat here is rarely too sticky as sea breezes offset the humidity. ▣ Take light clothing with cover-ups for the odd chilly winter evening.

St John's
Alt: 8m (25ft)

	J	F	M	A	M	J	J	A	S	O	N	D
Rainfall												
Comfort												
Sun hrs	8	8	9	9	9	9	9	9	9	8	8	8

Climate   **Tropical Oceanic**

Argentina

Capital City: **Buenos Aires**   World Map ref: **C6**   (In southern hemisphere)

This vast country, which is almost as large as India, has a varied topography and climate. Northernmost Argentina is tropical which means high temperatures and high humidity in the summer months (November to March) and rain throughout the year. Central Argentina, which includes Buenos Aires and the Pampas to the east, has a healthy and pleasant climate which is warm but fairly rainy in the summer and mild in the winter. Further west and to the south, the climate is sunny and drier and drought can occasionally be a problem. Western Argentina, including the northern Andes, is a dry region: even on the mountain peaks, which rise as high as 7,000m (23,000 ft), rain and snowfall is low. What rain there is falls mainly during the summer months which are very sunny and hot. This climate makes the eastern slopes and foothills of the Andes very arid while the surrounding lowlands are desert. Southern Argentina (also known as Patagonia) is largely dry but temperatures are cooler and the far south has chilly summers and long winters with plenty of frost and snow. However, the region's proximity to the Atlantic Ocean stops temperatures falling unbearably low.
▣ Pack light cotton clothes for northern and western Argentina (unless going high up into the Andes) and for central Argentina in their summer. Take warmer wear for central districts in winter and summer visits to the south. Wrap up very warmly for the winter months in southern Argentina. Even dry western Argentina experiences some rain, so go prepared.

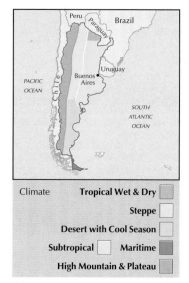

Climate   **Tropical Wet & Dry**

Steppe

Desert with Cool Season

Subtropical   **Maritime**

High Mountain & Plateau

Buenos Aires
Alt: 25m (80ft)

	J	F	M	A	M	J	J	A	S	O	N	D
Rainfall												
Comfort												
Sun hrs	9	9	7	7	6	4	5	6	6	8	9	9

Armenia

Capital City: **Yerevan**   World Map ref: **F2**

Armenia, which features Mount Ararat of Noah's Ark fame, is a small mountainous country whose summers are a joy. Its inhabitants bask in up to 12 hours of sunshine and high temperatures every day, although nights can

World Climate Map
see pages 6-7

	mm	5	25	75	150	300+
	in	0.2	1	3	6	12+

be chilly. Rainfall is light from June to September. Winters are a different story: they are extremely cold with heavy snowfalls. ◧ Even in the summer you will need warm clothing for the evenings. In winter, go prepared for high mountain conditions.

Yerevan
Alt: 910m (3,000ft)

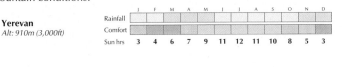

	J	F	M	A	M	J	J	A	S	O	N	D
Rainfall												
Comfort												
Sun hrs	3	4	6	7	9	11	12	11	10	8	5	3

Climate   **High Mountain & Plateau** ▨

Australia

Capital City: **Canberra**   World Map ref: **I6-J6**   (In southern hemisphere)

This island continent is almost as large as the United States and, since weather conditions vary substantially from region to region, we have broken the weather guide down into specific areas. Remember that Australian summers and winters are the reverse of those in Europe, so summer, broadly speaking, is the period from October to March, while April to September are the winter months for Australians.

Central Australia

Every Australian state, with the sole exception of Victoria, borders this very extensive desert region of central and western Australia, an arid, sparsely populated place which is the fiery heart of the continent and includes Alice Springs and Ayers Rock. Sunshine reigns nearly every day here, averaging 10 hours throughout the year, and rainfall is very sparse, falling in the south during the winter months (April to September) and in the north during the summer period (October to March). The climate here is the hot desert type, fringed by Steppe, with very hot summers and cooler winters, the hot dusty days giving way to chilly nights. ◧ Take a mixture of light clothing and warm cover-ups for the nights if you are travelling in this part of Australia.

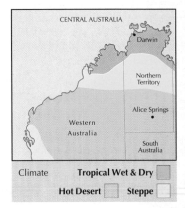

CENTRAL AUSTRALIA

Climate   **Tropical Wet & Dry** ▨
   Hot Desert ☐   **Steppe** ☐

Alice Springs
Alt: 580m (1,900ft)

	J	F	M	A	M	J	J	A	S	O	N	D
Rainfall												
Comfort												
Sun hrs	10	11	10	10	8	9	9	10	10	10	11	10

North & Northeast Australia

The north and northeast of Australia, which includes the coastal regions from Darwin in the Northern Territory round to Cairns and the Great Barrier Reef and extends almost down to Brisbane, has a tropical climate and is hot and sunny throughout the year. The monsoon rains arrive between November and March bringing torrential downpours and high humidity and making the coastal areas sticky and oppressive, although you'll still see 6 or 7 hours of sunshine a day. The northern coasts are hit by tropical cyclones (known as the "Willy Willies") several times a year. ◧ Light clothing is fine but you'll need rainwear between November and March and, down towards Brisbane, be prepared for rain at any time of the year.

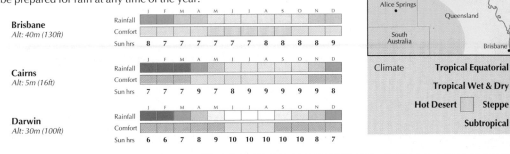

NORTH & NORTHEAST AUSTRALIA

Brisbane
Alt: 40m (130ft)

	J	F	M	A	M	J	J	A	S	O	N	D
Rainfall												
Comfort												
Sun hrs	8	7	7	7	7	7	7	8	8	8	8	9

Cairns
Alt: 5m (16ft)

	J	F	M	A	M	J	J	A	S	O	N	D
Rainfall												
Comfort												
Sun hrs	7	7	7	9	7	8	9	9	9	9	9	8

Darwin
Alt: 30m (100ft)

	J	F	M	A	M	J	J	A	S	O	N	D
Rainfall												
Comfort												
Sun hrs	6	6	7	8	9	10	10	10	10	10	8	7

Climate   **Tropical Equatorial** ▨
   Tropical Wet & Dry ▨
   Hot Desert ☐   **Steppe** ☐
   Subtropical ▨

Cold but tolerable   Hot but tolerable   Danger of Heatstroke

Extremely Cold   Comfortable, Temperate   Hot & Sticky, Very Hot

Key to Comfort

Australia - *continued*

Southeastern Australia

Southeastern Australia, which includes Sydney and Melbourne, very rarely experiences cold weather but can be rainy at any time of year. Summer temperatures (October to March) range from warm to hot on the coast to hot in the interior, which can suffer long spells of drought. However, while winter can bring cold spells to the interior, they are rare and brief on the coast. Weather throughout the region can be very changeable with coastal areas particularly subject to rain and cloudy conditions. Summer temperatures in Sydney and Melbourne can occasionally soar above 38°C (100°F) so try not to rush about outdoors too much during a very hot spell.
Take light clothing plus some slightly warmer clothing for the winter, although you'll need heavier attire if travelling inland to Canberra. Be prepared for rain in the coastal regions.

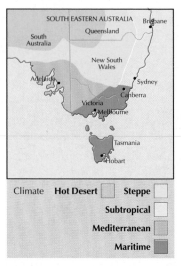

Climate	Hot Desert		Steppe	
			Subtropical	
			Mediterranean	
			Maritime	

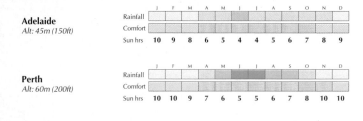

Melbourne
Alt: 35m (110ft)

	J	F	M	A	M	J	J	A	S	O	N	D
Rainfall												
Comfort												
Sun hrs	8	8	6	5	4	3	4	4	5	6	6	7

Sydney
Alt: 40m (130ft)

	J	F	M	A	M	J	J	A	S	O	N	D
Rainfall												
Comfort												
Sun hrs	7	7	6	6	6	5	6	7	7	8	7	8

Southern & Western Australia

Southern and western Australia, which include the cities of Perth and Adelaide, have a Mediterranean-type climate with moderate rainfall falling mainly in the winter period (April to September) when the weather can be quirky. Cyclones occasionally blow in and cause strong winds. Winter temperatures, however, are mild and nearly always well above freezing, averaging around 13°C (55°F). Perth is rainier than Adelaide and, in the summer (October to March), you should go prepared for bouts of extremely hot weather: inland temperatures can soar as high as 43°C (110°F).
Take light clothes and headgear for the summer and warmer wear and rain cover in the winter months.

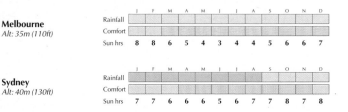

Climate	Hot Desert		Steppe	
			Mediterranean	

Adelaide
Alt: 45m (150ft)

	J	F	M	A	M	J	J	A	S	O	N	D
Rainfall												
Comfort												
Sun hrs	10	9	8	6	5	4	4	5	6	7	8	9

Perth
Alt: 60m (200ft)

	J	F	M	A	M	J	J	A	S	O	N	D
Rainfall												
Comfort												
Sun hrs	10	10	9	7	6	5	5	6	7	8	10	10

Tasmania

Tasmania, an island off the south coast of Australia, has a wetter, cloudier and generally cooler climate than the mainland and its weather is similar to that of the British Isles. Pack a mixture of light and fairly warm clothes for travelling here and always anticipate rain.

Hobart
Alt: 55m (180ft)

	J	F	M	A	M	J	J	A	S	O	N	D
Rainfall												
Comfort												
Sun hrs	8	7	6	5	4	4	4	5	6	6	7	7

Monthly Rainfall

mm	5	25	75	150	300+
in	0.2	1	3	6	12+

Austria

Capital City: **Vienna**   World Map ref: **F2**

One of the most mountainous areas in Europe, Austria is, not surprisingly, popular with wintersports enthusiasts. The Alps in winter are a great place to be, provided you stay high up. Conditions in mountain resorts are usually sunny and crisp while the valleys below are often shrouded in cloud and fog. In the summer, the opposite applies and the valleys bask in bright sunshine while the mountains are veiled in mist. In the southeast of Austria, the hills attract as much winter snow as those in the north but summertime conditions are more pleasant, with long bouts of brilliant sunshine. Always expect the unexpected here: the weather can quickly become unsettled and sudden thunderstorms may arise. The Danube Valley and the Vienna Basin are a good option for sunlovers since they enjoy a drier climate and plenty of summer sunshine. ⬛ Light clothes are fine in the summer but should be supplemented with warm wraps, and be prepared for summer rain. In the winter, sturdy skiwear is the order of the day.

Climate   **Continental**

High Mountain & Plateau

Vienna
Alt: 205m (670ft)

	J	F	M	A	M	J	J	A	S	O	N	D
Rainfall												
Comfort												
Sun hrs	2	3	4	6	8	8	9	8	6	4	2	1

Azerbaijan

Capital City: **Baku**   World Map ref: **G2**

The Caspian Sea provides Azerbaijan with its eastern coastline while the country's inland central plains roll up into the Caucasus Mountain ranges. This topography produces a varied climate. Long, hot summers and mild winters prevail in the lowlands which experience little rain all year. Up in the mountains, winters are extremely cold with heavy snowfalls in the north and west. ⬛ Light clothes are fine from May to September but take warmer attire for the rest of the year.

Baku
Alt: 5m (16ft)

	J	F	M	A	M	J	J	A	S	O	N	D
Rainfall												
Comfort												
Sun hrs	3	3	3	4	7	8	8	7	5	4	4	3

Climate   **Steppe**

High Mountain & Plateau

Azores *see under* **Portugal**

Bahamas

Capital City: **Nassau**   World Map ref: **C3**

The Bahamas are the most northerly of the Caribbean islands. They comprise some 700 tropical coral islands, only 30 of which are inhabited, together with more than 1,000 small islands or reefs known as Cays. There is some rain all year but the wettest months are from May to October. In the northern islands (including Nassau on New Providence), winter temperatures can, on occasion, drop below 15°C (60°F) as a result of colder continental air blowing down from North America. Summers are hotter and more humid with an average of 9 hours of daily sunshine. Hurricanes can hit between July and November. ⬛ Pack light clothing with cover-ups for chilly winter spells.

Nassau
Alt: 3m (10ft)

	J	F	M	A	M	J	J	A	S	O	N	D
Rainfall												
Comfort												
Sun hrs	7	8	9	9	9	8	9	9	7	7	7	7

Climate   **Tropical Oceanic**

Cold but tolerable	Hot but tolerable	Danger of Heatstroke
Extremely Cold	Comfortable, Temperate	Hot & Sticky, Very Hot

Key to Comfort

Bahrain

Capital City: **Manama**   World Map ref: **G3**

High temperatures and humidity make life in Bahrain a misery in the summer months when conditions are so hot and sticky there is a danger of heat exhaustion for the unwary. Winter temperatures are more comfortable, making this a better time to visit, although nights can be chilly and cold winds can gust in from Iran. Rainfall is sparse and occurs mainly in the winter months.  If you must go in the summer, take very light, loose clothing and keep your head covered. Take slightly warmer clothing for the winter months.

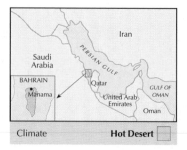

Climate   **Hot Desert**

Manama
Alt: 2m (7ft)

	J	F	M	A	M	J	J	A	S	O	N	D
Rainfall												
Comfort												
Sun hrs	8	9	9	8	10	10	10	11	10	10	8	7

Balearic Islands *see under* **Spain**

The Baltic States

Capital City: **Tallinn, Riga, Vilnius**   World Map ref: **F2**

The three small republics of Estonia, Latvia and Lithuania comprise the Baltic States, which lie on the northwest boundary of Russia and share elements of that vast country's climate. Fortunately, the proximity of the Baltic Sea (which rarely freezes for long periods) keeps temperatures fairly moderate and saves them from the worst excesses of the freezing Russian winter. That said, the months from November to March are hard going with heavy snowfalls and ferocious winter winds which howl straight in from the heart of the Russian interior. Unless you enjoy dressing like Nanook of the North, arrange your visit during the summer months when temperatures are warm, with up to 10 hours of sunshine a day. Rainfall is highest in August; spring and autumn are mild but rainy.  Take light clothing with warm cover-ups and rainwear in the summer. Pack thermals and very heavy clothes for a winter visit!

Climate   **Continental**

Tallinn, Estonia
Alt: 45m (150ft)

	J	F	M	A	M	J	J	A	S	O	N	D
Rainfall												
Comfort												
Sun hrs	1	2	4	6	7	11	10	8	5	2	1	0

Riga, Latvia
Alt: 3m (10ft)

	J	F	M	A	M	J	J	A	S	O	N	D
Rainfall												
Comfort												
Sun hrs	1	2	4	6	7	11	10	9	6	3	1	1

Vilnius, Lithuania
Alt: 190m (620ft)

	J	F	M	A	M	J	J	A	S	O	N	D
Rainfall												
Comfort												
Sun hrs	1	2	4	6	7	10	10	9	6	3	1	1

Bangladesh

Capital City: **Dhaka**   World Map ref: **H3**

Stories of floods in Bangladesh have for decades made headline news. This low-lying country, which lies at the head of the Bay of Bengal, has one of the world's rainiest climates, receiving an average of 2,500mm (100in) a year.

World Climate Map
see pages 6-7

Monthly Rainfall

mm	5	25	75	150	300+
in	0.2	1	3	6	12+

Bangladesh - *continued*

Temperatures are highest during the April to October rainy season and these combine with high humidity to produce a stifling, sultry heat which is very trying. Thunderstorms are frequent during the early part of the rains (April to June) but the most dangerous time to be in Bangladesh is during the latter part of the southwest monsoon, in September and October. At this time, devastating cyclones can arise bringing gale force winds and ferocious downpours, whipping up coastal seas to cause extensive flooding of low-lying areas and often with considerable loss of life. The rains tail off in November when the cool season begins and, until its end in February, life in Bangladesh is rather more tolerable. This is the period of maximum sunshine (the sun is obscured by very heavy cloud during the rains) and temperatures are warm although evenings can be chilly. 📷 Take light clothes for a trip to Bangladesh supplemented with warmer wraps for evenings during the cool season and be prepared for heavy rain if you are visiting during the monsoon period.

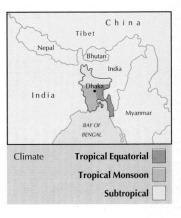

Climate   **Tropical Equatorial**

Tropical Monsoon

Subtropical

Dhaka
Alt: 8m (25ft)

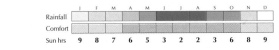

	J	F	M	A	M	J	J	A	S	O	N	D
Rainfall												
Comfort												
Sun hrs	9	8	7	6	5	3	2	2	3	6	8	9

Barbados

Capital City: **Bridgetown**   World Map ref: **C4**

Barbados is the most easterly of the Windward Islands and can find itself in the path of hurricanes between July and November. It has some rain throughout the year but not as much as neighbouring St Lucia and Martinique. Its wettest months are from June to November. Typically for the Caribbean, the island is consistently hot all year but temperatures are never extreme and sea breezes help to counter humidity. 📷 Light cotton clothing with cover-ups for the occasional chilly evening is appropriate for any time of the year, but don't wear beach clothes if you are going into town: the Barbadians don't like it.

Climate   **Tropical Oceanic**

Bridgetown
Alt: 55m (180ft)

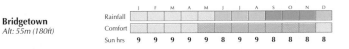

	J	F	M	A	M	J	J	A	S	O	N	D
Rainfall												
Comfort												
Sun hrs	9	9	9	9	9	8	9	9	8	8	8	8

Belarus

Capital City: **Minsk**   World Map ref: **F2**

Belarus lies between Poland on the West and European Russia on the East and its climate is typical of that which prevails throughout the northern and central regions of European Russia. This low-lying country experiences weather from the Atlantic and North-West Europe as well as Russia and the one thing you can be absolutely sure of is that winters will be freezing. With only an hour or two of daily sunshine to relieve the gloom, it is better to avoid this region in the winter months. Summers in Belarus are warm and frequently sunny with up to 10 hours of sunshine a day. However, summer is also the main season for rainfall. 📷 If you must visit Belarus in winter, take thermals and very warm clothing. Light clothes with warmer cover-ups are fine in the summer but always go prepared for rain.

Climate   **Continental**

Minsk
Alt: 230m (750ft)

	J	F	M	A	M	J	J	A	S	O	N	D
Rainfall												
Comfort												
Sun hrs	2	2	4	5	8	10	9	8	6	3	1	1

	Cold but tolerable		Hot but tolerable		Danger of Heatstroke	
Extremely Cold		Comfortable, Temperate		Hot & Sticky, Very Hot	

Key to Comfort

Belgium

Capital City: **Brussels** World Map ref: **E2**

Always be prepared for rain in Belgium as the weather is very changeable. The summer months (May to September) are generally warm with between 6 and 7 hours of sunshine a day. Central Belgium, which is hilly, is slightly warmer than the coast but pays for it with chillier winters. The Ardennes region in the south has the harshest winters with long periods of snow but its summers, although cooler than in other parts of the country, are fairly sunny and pleasant. British-style clothing is fine for most of the year but you will need to wrap up extra warmly to face winter in the Ardennes.

Brussels
Alt: 55m (180ft)

	J	F	M	A	M	J	J	A	S	O	N	D
Rainfall												
Comfort												
Sun hrs	2	3	4	5	6	7	6	6	5	4	2	1

Climate   **Maritime**

Belize

Capital City: **Belmopan** World Map ref: **B4**

One of the smaller countries of Central America, Belize has the Maya mountains in its southwest and a long, low-lying coastline fringing the Caribbean. June to November is the rainiest time and downpours can be torrential, especially if hurricanes and tropical storms hit town. There is the likelihood of coastal rain at any time of the year. The weather is very hot and humid all year although, on the coast, the stickiness is often dissipated by strong winds from the Caribbean. The best time to visit is during the drier season which stretches from January to April. Take light clothes and a light raincoat.

Belize City
Alt: 5m (16ft)

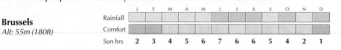

	J	F	M	A	M	J	J	A	S	O	N	D
Rainfall												
Comfort												
Sun hrs	4	5	5	4	3	3	3	3	3	3	3	3

Climate   **Tropical Equatorial**

Benin

Capital City: **Porto-Novo** World Map ref: **E4**

Benin's limited coastline, which borders the Gulf of Guinea, tends to be drier for most of the year than inland regions, partly because of cold sea currents. Temperatures vary from north to south. Northern districts enjoy very sunny, hot winters and cooler, very wet summers, while the south has two rainy and two dry seasons. Hot, arid conditions predominate from November to February and again during August, while the rains come from March to July and September to October. Light clothing is appropriate, backed up with rainwear during the rainy seasons and warmer wear for chilly winter evenings.

Cotonou
Alt: 5m (16ft)

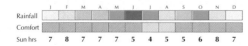

	J	F	M	A	M	J	J	A	S	O	N	D
Rainfall												
Comfort												
Sun hrs	7	8	7	7	7	5	4	5	5	6	8	7

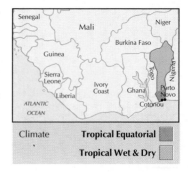

Climate   **Tropical Equatorial**

Tropical Wet & Dry

Bermuda

Capital City: **Hamilton** World Map ref: **C3**

World Climate Map
see pages 6-7

This lush North Atlantic island really is an earthly paradise: it has all the joys of a subtropical climate without the nuisance of a rainy season. When rain

mm	5	25	75	150	300+
in	0.2	1	3	6	12+

does fall, which it does in quantity, it has the good manners to fall mainly, and conveniently, at night. May to mid-November are the sunniest months on the island with temperatures reaching their peak (up to 30°C/86°F) in July, August and September. The winter months are cooler but mild with a good proportion of warm, sunny days. Between seasons the weather can be changeable, with hot and chilly days occurring in quick succession. In late summer, Bermuda can occasionally be affected by the tail end of hurricanes coming from the Caribbean.  Light clothing is fine for the summer months but in winter add warm cover-ups.

Hamilton
Alt: 45m (150ft)

	J	F	M	A	M	J	J	A	S	O	N	D
Rainfall												
Comfort												
Sun hrs	5	5	6	8	8	8	10	9	8	6	6	5

Climate   **Subtropical**

Bhutan

Capital City: **Thimphu**   World Map ref: **H3**

Bhutan, a small mountainous country in the Himalayas, has a seasonal climate and conditions vary with altitude, temperatures falling deeper the higher up you go. In the spring and autumn, rainfall is lower and days, although bright and sunny, are pleasantly warm rather than hot. The mountain foothills are the best place to be in the winter months: higher up, the weather can be very cold. However, even in the lower reaches, you should go prepared for very chilly nights.  If you are staying low in the mountains, take light clothes for the day with warmer wraps for the evenings and always be prepared for rain. However, if you are going high up into the mountains, take much warmer attire.

Thimphu
Alt: 2,990m (9,800ft)

	J	F	M	A	M	J	J	A	S	O	N	D
Rainfall												
Comfort												
Sun hrs	6	6	8	6	5	2	2	3	5	10	10	9

Climate   **High Mountain & Plateau**

Bolivia

Capital City: **La Paz**   World Map ref: **C5**   (In southern hemisphere)

This large, landlocked country is twice the size of France and is a land of two climates. In its west, the great peaks of the Andes soar up to 6,000m (20,000ft) and even the plateau which lies between the eastern and western ranges of these mighty mountains stands between 3,000m (10,000ft) and 4,000m (13,000ft) high. However, as you move east of the Andes, the land descends dramatically into the rainforests of the Amazon Basin and to lowlands further south. The lowlands have a hot, steamy tropical climate with a single, heavy rainy season from November to February when temperatures are highest. In the mountains, it's a different story: temperatures drop lower the higher up you go. The northeast slopes of the Andes are semi-tropical but, on higher ground, night time temperatures can be extremely cold and frosts are frequent during the dry season. The high peaks are permanently snowcapped. On the plateau between the high mountains, rainfall is low and occurs mainly from December to March. The two main hazards you'll encounter here are altitude sickness and sunburn: the air is very thin in the mountains so you should be prepared to acclimatise slowly.
 Pack light cotton clothes as well as a light raincoat and take much warmer clothing for the mountains.

La Paz
Alt: 3,660m (12,000ft)

	J	F	M	A	M	J	J	A	S	O	N	D
Rainfall												
Comfort												
Sun hrs	6	5	5	6	8	9	9	8	7	6	6	6

Climate   **Tropical Equatorial**

Tropical Wet & Dry

High Mountain & Plateau

	Cold but tolerable		Hot but tolerable		Danger of Heatstroke	
Extremely Cold		Comfortable, Temperate		Hot & Sticky, Very Hot		Key to Comfort

Bosnia - Hercegovina

Capital City: **Sarajevo** World Map ref: **F2**

With a mountainous interior and large rivers to its north and east, the climate of Bosnia-Herzegovinia is similar to that of Eastern Europe: broadly hot in the summer, very cold in the winter but changeable all year round. The mountains can attract heavy rain at any time and winters can be fierce with snow lying in the hills for long periods. The north is, by and large, colder and rainier than the south. ▇ Take very warm clothing and waterproofs in the winter. In the summer, lightweight clothing is fine unless you are heading for the north where warmer clothing will be needed.

Sarajevo
Alt: 630m (2,050ft)

	J	F	M	A	M	J	J	A	S	O	N	D
Rainfall												
Comfort												
Sun hrs	2	3	4	5	6	8	9	9	7	4	2	2

Climate   **Continental**

Botswana

Capital City: **Gaborone** World Map ref: **F6** (In southern hemisphere)

Except in its northeast, Botswana is largely desert or semi-desert and, consequently, receives very low levels of rainfall. The rainy season (from November to March) brings very high temperatures and only sporadic downpours which are much lighter in the south and west. From May to September, cooler weather prevails and nights can be nippy with occasional frosts. ▇ A mixture of light and warm clothing for the cooler nights is recommended.

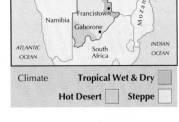

Francistown
Alt: 1,005m (3,300ft)

	J	F	M	A	M	J	J	A	S	O	N	D
Rainfall												
Comfort												
Sun hrs	7	8	8	9	9	10	9	10	10	9	8	8

Climate   **Tropical Wet & Dry**

Hot Desert   **Steppe**

Brazil

Capital City: **Brasilia** World Map ref: **C5-D5** (In southern hemisphere)

Brazil is massive. It is larger than the United States and contains almost half the land mass of South America, although it does not include the Andes within its borders. Most of the country lies within the tropics and has a hot, steamy climate. The largest regions are the Amazon Basin, which occupies the north and centre of Brazil, and the Brazilian plateau, which includes Brasilia and lies to the south and east of the Basin. Then there is the narrow Atlantic coastal plain and the country's southern states which, because they lie outside the tropics, have a temperate climate and can be chilly in the winter months (May to September). Rainy seasons vary from region to region. In the Amazon Basin, which is the world's largest equatorial area, the rains come mainly between December and April although there can be downpours at any time of the year. The northeast is much drier with unpredictable rainfall from year to year. Recife, at the top of the Atlantic coastal plain, has its wettest months from April to August whereas Rio, at the bottom end, is moderately wet all year with heavier rainfall between November and April. The southern states experience some rain throughout the year. ▇ Pack light cotton clothes and waterproofs geared to the region you are visiting. Take warmer wear for visits to the south, if you are travelling between May and September, and sturdy boots as well as plenty of insect repellent if visiting the Amazon.

Climate   **Tropical Equatorial**

Tropical Wet & Dry

Steppe   **Subtropical**

Rio de Janeiro
Alt: 5m (16ft)

	J	F	M	A	M	J	J	A	S	O	N	D
Rainfall												
Comfort												
Sun hrs	7	7	7	6	6	6	6	7	5	5	6	6

Monthly Rainfall

mm		5		25		75		150		300+
in		0.2		1		3		6		12+

British Virgin Islands *see under* Virgin Islands

Brunei Darussalam

Capital City: **Bandar Seri Begawan** World Map ref: **I4**

This tiny, very wealthy country, which has a coastal plain on the South China Sea, mountains in the east and tropical rainforest covering 75 per cent of its surface, is very hot all year with average temperatures up in the high 20s Centigrade (low 80s Fahrenheit). It experiences very heavy rainfall from April to December and no time of year can guarantee dry weather.
 Light clothing is essential at any time of the year but so are waterproofs.

Bandar Seri Begawan
Alt: 20m (65ft)

	J	F	M	A	M	J	J	A	S	O	N	D
Rainfall												
Comfort												
Sun hrs	7	8	8	9	7	7	7	7	6	7	7	7

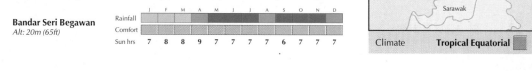

Climate   **Tropical Equatorial**

Bulgaria

Capital City: **Sofia** World Map ref: **F2**

What you pack for Bulgaria depends on which part of the country you plan to visit, and when. On the Black Sea Coast, you can find yourself basking in Mediterranean-type temperatures in the summer, while winter could leave you shivering in the face of icy winds from Russia. Although coastal winters are largely mild, they can suddenly be interrupted by cold spells ferocious enough to freeze the mighty River Danube. Even in the summer, hot, sunny days on the coast can suddenly give way to squalls and thunderstorms with torrential rain and even hail. Inland from the coast, you can expect warm to hot summers and cold winters. Up in the mountains, summer temperatures are cooler but sunshine is plentiful; winters are cold, crisp and snowy. Wherever you are in Bulgaria, temperatures can become extreme and springtime is the most unsettled period. Even at the height of summer, it is advisable to take warm clothes to supplement lightweight outfits. In the winter, warm clothing is essential. Be prepared for rain at any time.

Sofia
Alt: 550m (1,800ft)

	J	F	M	A	M	J	J	A	S	O	N	D
Rainfall												
Comfort												
Sun hrs	2	3	4	6	7	9	10	10	7	5	3	1

Climate   **Mediterranean**

Continental

Burkina Faso

Capital City: **Ouagadougou** World Map ref: **E4**

This landlocked country has a tropical climate with a single rainy season from May to September followed by a long, dry season. Conditions are at their best from November to February when the Harmattan desert winds disperse the usual humidity and create cooler, crisper but still sunny weather. A downside is that the Harmattan can be very dusty, so take scarves to protect nose and mouth if you are travelling at this time. Lightweight clothing is appropriate at any time of year along with waterproofs during the rainy season, particularly for the southwest where rainfall is heaviest.

Ouagadougou
Alt: 305m (1,000ft)

	J	F	M	A	M	J	J	A	S	O	N	D
Rainfall												
Comfort												
Sun hrs	9	9	9	8	9	8	7	6	7	9	9	8

Climate   **Tropical Wet & Dry**

Steppe

Cold but tolerable	Hot but tolerable	Danger of Heatstroke	
Extremely Cold	Comfortable, Temperate	Hot & Sticky, Very Hot	Key to Comfort

Burma *see under* Myanmar

Burundi

Capital City: **Bujumbura** World Map ref: **F5** (In southern hemisphere)

Burundi is a mountainous land and, in its higher altitudes, temperatures are chilly. Hot, sunny conditions prevail in the dry months (June to September) but the rest of the year is moderately wet. Humidity levels rise during the rainy season but, overall, conditions are pleasant.  Take light clothing for the daytime and wraps for cooler evenings.

Bujumbura
Alt: 780m (2,550ft)

	J	F	M	A	M	J	J	A	S	O	N	D
Rainfall												
Comfort												
Sun hrs	5	5	6	5	7	8	9	8	7	6	5	5

Climate   **Tropical Wet & Dry**

Cambodia

Capital City: **Phnom Penh** World Map ref: **H4**

This small country lies within the tropics and has a monsoon climate with rains arriving in May and lasting until October. Rainfall is heaviest in the southwestern hills and on the slopes surrounding the Gulf of Thailand. The rainy season brings cloudy days, hot and humid conditions and the risk of heat exhaustion. From December to April, the weather is largely hot and sunny although temperatures can fall quite low in the northern hills.
 Take light clothes, whatever the time of year, supplemented by warmer wear if you are travelling north in the winter and waterproofs for the rains.

Phnom Penh
Alt: 10m (35ft)

	J	F	M	A	M	J	J	A	S	O	N	D
Rainfall												
Comfort												
Sun hrs	9	9	9	8	7	6	6	6	5	7	8	9

Climate   **Tropical Monsoon**

Cameroon

Capital City: **Yaoundé** World Map ref: **E4**

Only visit the south of Cameroon if you don't mind rain: it can bucket down at any time of year but is particularly heavy between March and October. Parts of the Cameroon Peak have the highest recorded rainfall in the world! The rain eases off between December and February when conditions improve to become sunnier and drier. The north of the country has one wet season from May to September and a long dry season. 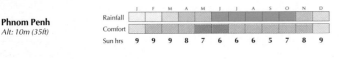 Take light clothing and don't forget the rainwear!

Douala
Alt: 10m (35ft)

	J	F	M	A	M	J	J	A	S	O	N	D
Rainfall												
Comfort												
Sun hrs	5	6	5	5	5	3	2	1	2	4	5	5

Climate   **Tropical Equatorial**

Tropical Wet & Dry

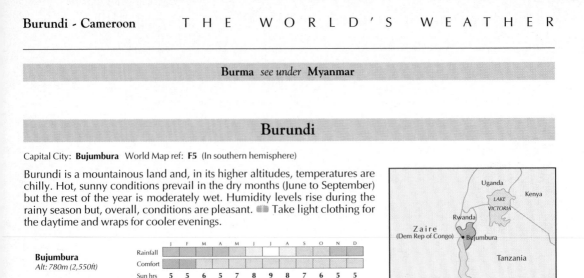

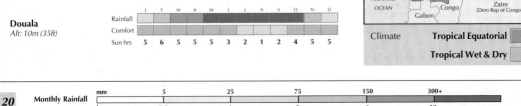

Monthly Rainfall	mm	5	25	75	150	300+
	in	0.2	1	3	6	12+

Canada

Capital City: **Ottawa**   World Map ref: **B2-C2**

Western Canada

Western Canada, which comprises southern British Columbia and the western part of Alberta (including the Canadian Rockies), is a mountainous region with a coastline on the Pacific Ocean and a climate as varied as its terrain. The coastal mountains experience very heavy rainfall, much of it falling as snow, but the inland plateau and valleys are protected from harsh weather by the mountains and have a largely dry climate. The coast has warm, sunny summers and the mildest winter climate in the whole of Canada but it gets a substantial amount of winter rain and plenty of fog so winter weather can be gloomy and changeable. Inland, winters are dryer but much harsher with freezing frosts in the valleys and snow above 1,200m (4,000 ft). ▪️ Take fairly warm (UK-style) clothes for visiting the coast in winter but wrap up much more heavily if you are going inland and/or visiting the mountains. Pack rainwear for winter visits. Lighter clothes for the summer should be supplemented with wraps.

Climate	**Steppe**		**Maritime**	
	Continental		**Subarctic**	
	High Mountain & Plateau			

Vancouver		J	F	M	A	M	J	J	A	S	O	N	D
Alt: 5m (16ft)	Rainfall												
	Comfort												
	Sun hrs	2	3	4	6	8	7	9	8	6	4	3	2

Eastern Canada

Eastern Canada, which includes the island of Newfoundland, the Labrador Coast and the maritime provinces of New Brunswick, Prince Edward Island and Nova Scotia, has cold winters and, because of its proximity to the Atlantic ocean, changeable summers. You really need to be prepared for anything if you visit this part of the world: the weather can change dramatically from day to day. Expect plenty of rain and cloud at any time of year, snow in winter and sea fogs during the summer months. Sunshine is at a premium in winter when the region gets only 3 to 4 hours a day; summers are brighter with 7 to 8 hours of sun. ▪️ Pack fairly warm clothing for a summer visit and wrap up very warmly if you are travelling in the winter. Take a raincoat whenever you go!

Climate	**Continental**	
	Subarctic	

Halifax		J	F	M	A	M	J	J	A	S	O	N	D
Alt: 25m (80ft)	Rainfall												
	Comfort												
	Sun hrs	3	4	5	5	6	7	8	7	6	5	3	3

Southern Regions

The southern regions of Quebec and Ontario border the Great Lakes; vast bodies of fresh water which make this the warmest and sunniest part of Canada, in the summer. However, winters can be severe. The lakes freeze over in late December and heavy snows persist from December to March but there are surprisingly mild spells which will thaw the snow even in the depths of winter. Conversely, cyclonic storms can make summer weather very unsettled and bring sudden cold, wet spells. ▪️ Pack light clothes supplemented with warm cover-ups for a summer visit but wrap up very well in the winter: take thermal underwear, sturdy boots, earmuffs, the lot. Be prepared for rain whatever the time of year.

Montreal		J	F	M	A	M	J	J	A	S	O	N	D
Alt: 30m (100ft)	Rainfall												
	Comfort												
	Sun hrs	3	4	5	5	7	8	8	8	6	4	2	2

Toronto		J	F	M	A	M	J	J	A	S	O	N	D
Alt: 115m (380ft)	Rainfall												
	Comfort												
	Sun hrs	2	4	4	6	7	9	9	8	7	5	3	2

Climate	**Continental**	
	Subarctic	

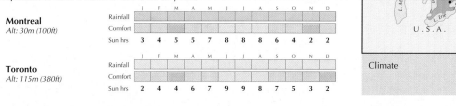

	Cold but tolerable		Hot but tolerable		Danger of Heatstroke	
Extremely Cold		Comfortable, Temperate		Hot & Sticky, Very Hot		Key to Comfort

The Canadian Prairies

The Canadian Prairies, which range from the Rocky Mountains to the western shores of Lake Superior and include the southern parts of Alberta, Manitoba and Saskatchewan, have a Continental-type climate. This means long, extremely harsh winters and short, warm, showery summers when 9 to 10 hours of daily sunshine can be recorded. The main problem in the winter is not so much snow, which is relatively sparse, but strong often freezing winds. The cities of Calgary and Edmonton, which lie near the Canadian Rockies, enjoy slightly higher winter temperatures because of the warm Chinook wind which occasionally gusts down from over the mountains, thawing snow for a day or two. This means that average temperatures only plunge as low as minus 20°C (-4°F)! Winnipeg, which gets no such relief from the mountain winds, frequently clocks up winter temperatures lower than minus 25°C (-13°F). 👕 Pack like Nanook of the North if you are planning a winter trip to this region. In the summer, supplement light clothes with warm cover-ups for the evenings.

Climate	Continental
	Subarctic

Winnipeg
Alt: 240m (790ft)

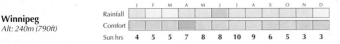

	J	F	M	A	M	J	J	A	S	O	N	D
Rainfall												
Comfort												
Sun hrs	4	5	5	7	8	8	10	9	6	5	3	3

Northern Regions

Two thirds of this giant country, its northern regions, are made virtually uninhabitable by extreme winter weather comparable in its harshness to that of Siberia. The extreme north includes the Yukon and Northwest territories and the northern reaches of British Columbia, Alberta, Saskatchewan, Manitoba, Ontario and Quebec and it really is a land of ice and snow. The islands of the Arctic archipelago, which lie to the west of Greenland, are snow-covered throughout the year. The remainder of this vast region has a subarctic climate which brings snow for around 8 months of the year although the very short summer can bring surprisingly high temperatures. However, summer weather is largely unsettled and cold winds, howling down from the Polar regions, can bring sudden frost and flurries of snow. 👕 If you must visit, try to stick to the summer months and wrap up warmly even then. In winter, take heavy thermal clothing and try to avoid being out of doors for long periods: wind chill is ferocious and can cause frostbite or worse.

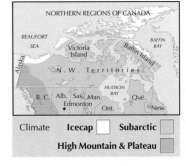

Climate	Icecap		Subarctic
High Mountain & Plateau			

Canary Islands *see under* **Spain**

Cape Verde

Capital City: **Praia** World Map ref: **D4**

These ten volcanic islands, which lie off the west coast of Africa, have some fine beaches and enjoy a tropical oceanic climate. Rainfall is very low outside the August to October rainy season and temperatures are consistently high throughout the year. Humidity can cause discomfort during the rainy months. 👕 Pack light clothing whenever you visit and be prepared for rain between August and October.

Climate	Tropical Oceanic

Praia
Alt: 25m (80ft)

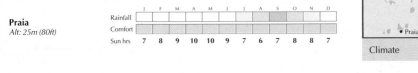

	J	F	M	A	M	J	J	A	S	O	N	D
Rainfall												
Comfort												
Sun hrs	7	8	9	10	10	9	7	6	7	8	8	7

mm		5	25	75	150	300+
Monthly Rainfall						
in		0.2	1	3	6	12+

Cayman Islands

Capital City: Georgetown World Map ref: **C4**

Grand Cayman is the largest and most well known of these three low-lying Cayman Islands which lie due south of Cuba. Trade winds blow softly here making conditions particularly pleasant and balmy and even the rains are of the "liquid sunshine" variety with short, intense showers sandwiched between periods of brilliant sunshine. The wettest months are May to November and, at this time, there is a chance of tropical storms or hurricanes hitting town. Temperatures are consistently hot all year but never excessive. Light cotton clothing at any time of the year with cover-ups for occasional chilly winter evenings is appropriate.

Grand Cayman
Alt: 6m (20ft)

	J	F	M	A	M	J	J	A	S	O	N	D
Rainfall												
Comfort												
Sun hrs	8	8	9	9	8	8	9	8	7	7	8	7

Climate   **Tropical Oceanic**

Central African Republic

Capital City: Bangui World Map ref: **F4**

This landlocked country is hot all year round with temperatures soaring highest in its northeastern corner. Rainfall is moderate in the north occurring between May and September. Further south, the rains are heavier and can occur at any time of year although the highest concentration is between July and October. December to February is the dry season with an average of 7 hours sunshine a day. Light clothing is recommended.

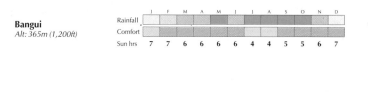

Bangui
Alt: 365m (1,200ft)

	J	F	M	A	M	J	J	A	S	O	N	D
Rainfall												
Comfort												
Sun hrs	7	7	6	6	6	6	4	4	5	5	6	7

Climate   **Tropical Equatorial**

Tropical Wet & Dry

Chad

Capital City: Ndjamena World Map ref: **F4**

Chad's northern half lies in the Sahara Desert and is subsequently very hot all year round with very little rain. Further south (in the Sahel region) there is a rainy season during the period of high sun from May to September. The region has 6 to 7 daily hours of sunshine during the rainy season and up to 11 hours during the dry period. If you are travelling during the dry season, take warm clothes to combat chilly night temperatures and frequent strong winds.

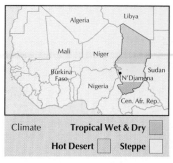

Ndjamena
Alt: 295m (970ft)

	J	F	M	A	M	J	J	A	S	O	N	D
Rainfall												
Comfort												
Sun hrs	11	10	9	9	9	8	7	6	7	9	10	11

Climate   **Tropical Wet & Dry**

Hot Desert   **Steppe**

Cold but tolerable	Hot but tolerable	Danger of Heatstroke
Extremely Cold	Comfortable, Temperate	Hot & Sticky, Very Hot

Key to Comfort

Channel Islands

Capital City: **St Helier, St Peter Port**   World Map ref: **E2**

These holiday islands have a delightfully warm summer climate and enjoy mild, if rainy, winters. On the long summer days, between May and September, you can bask in an average of 8 hours of sunshine a day but, if you are planning a walk or a visit to the beach, take a cover-up as those sea breezes can be chilly. Rain falls mainly in the autumn and winter but can occur sporadically in the summer months. Winters are cool but rarely very cold. ▪▪ Take relatively warm clothing for the cool winter months and, in the summer, supplement beach wear and light clothing with a warm wrap, just in case. Be prepared for rain at any time of year.

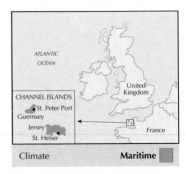

Jersey - St Helier
Alt: 10m (35ft)

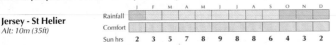

	J	F	M	A	M	J	J	A	S	O	N	D
Rainfall												
Comfort												
Sun hrs	2	3	5	7	8	9	8	8	6	4	3	2

Climate   **Maritime** ▪

Chile

Capital City: **Santiago**   World Map ref: **C6**   (In southern hemisphere)

Chile, which spans more than 2,500 miles from north to south, is a long, narrow, rugged country with a range of climatic conditions to match its varied topography. Its north lies in the Atacama coastal desert which, although one of the world's driest regions, experiences a lot of cloud and mist. This obscures the sun and prevents the permanently high temperatures becoming excessive. The spine of the mighty Andes runs down Chile's eastern borders and its northern range has a typical mountain climate of crisp, thin air and light rainfall with permanent snow and ice on its higher reaches. Most of the population (not surprisingly) is based in the lowlands of central Chile which have a Mediterranean-type climate with warm, dry summers (November to March) and mild, rainy winters. The winter months can bring frost and snow inland but this rarely affects the coast. This is a sunny region in the summer, clocking up an average of 10 hours of daily sunshine. The Southern Andes is a region of much heavier snow and rainfall: snow can occur almost down to sea level. The wettest part of Chile is its south which has a cool maritime climate and rainfall throughout the year. Summers are cool, cloudy and changeable while winters vary from fairly mild, in more northerly districts, to very cold in the deep south. ▪▪ Pack light cotton clothes for visits to northern and Central Chile with warmer supplements for central Chilean winters. Take much heavier clothing for visits down south (especially in winter) and for trips up into the Andes. Go prepared for rain at any time if you are visiting the south or going to central Chile in the winter months (May to September).

Climate

Hot Desert ☐
Mediterranean ☐
Maritime ▪
High Mountain & Plateau ☐

Santiago
Alt: 520m (1,700ft)

	J	F	M	A	M	J	J	A	S	O	N	D
Rainfall												
Comfort												
Sun hrs	11	9	9	6	4	3	3	4	5	6	9	10

China

Capital City: **Beijing**   World Map ref: **H3-I3**

The world's second largest country has a wide range of topographical features and a climate which varies significantly from region to region.

Northern China
In the northeast, where Beijing (formerly Peking) lies, you'll find a typical Continental climate with warm to hot summers and freezing cold, very frosty

> Weather Statistics for 315
> locations around the world
> *see pages 94-103*

mm		5	25	75	150	300+
in		0.2	1	3	6	12+

China - continued

winters bringing occasional light snow. In the extreme north of Manchuria, winters are cold enough to freeze the rivers for up to six months. Summer temperatures are also cooler here than in the rest of Northern China where the summer months bring clammy, humid conditions and most of the annual rainfall. 🔲 You'll need very warm clothing to face Northern China and its windchill factor in the winter months. In the spring, summer and autumn light clothing should be supplemented with warmer cover-ups for chilly evenings and windy days. Be prepared for rain in the summer.

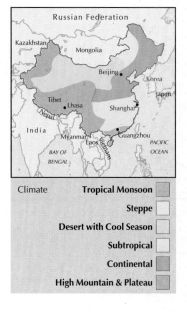

Beijing
Alt: 55m (180ft)

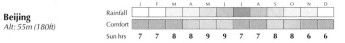

	J	F	M	A	M	J	J	A	S	O	N	D
Rainfall												
Comfort												
Sun hrs	7	7	8	8	9	9	7	7	8	8	6	6

Central China

Central China, where Shanghai is located, is warmer than the north in both summer and winter but it can rain at any time. Winter weather is very changeable, alternating between spells of heavy cloud and rain and bright but cold, frosty periods with occasional snow. The main rains come in the summer months when fronts from the Pacific usher in sticky, humid air which makes the heat unpleasant. Along the coasts, from July to October, you may find strong winds and very heavy rainfall as typhoons (tropical cyclones) blow in. One of the best areas to visit in central China is the Sichuan Basin of the Yangtse valley where winters are quite warm and summers less rainy and, therefore, lower in humidity. 🔲 Take light clothes for the summer but be prepared for chilly days if visiting the coast and remember it can rain at any time! Warm clothing is advisable in winter.

Shanghai
Alt: 8m (25ft)

	J	F	M	A	M	J	J	A	S	O	N	D
Rainfall												
Comfort												
Sun hrs	4	4	4	5	5	5	7	7	5	6	5	5

Southern China

Southern China, which contains Guangzhou (Canton), is the warmest and wettest part of the country in the summer because of its proximity to the tropics. Go prepared for very heavy rainfall between June and September, particularly on the coast where typhoons can strike. 🔲 Take light clothing as the summer humidity can be very oppressive. Winters are mild and you should be able to get away with a mixture of light clothes and warmer cover-ups.

The inland region of Southern China is mountainous with cooler summers and rain in the highlands. However, winters are sunny and warm with little rain and the valleys are largely dry even in the summer months. 🔲 Take light to medium clothing whatever the time of year with warmer attire if you are going up high.

Guangzhou - Canton
Alt: 8m (25ft)

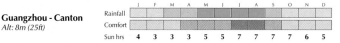

	J	F	M	A	M	J	J	A	S	O	N	D
Rainfall												
Comfort												
Sun hrs	4	3	3	3	5	5	7	7	7	7	6	5

Southwestern China

Tibet, which lies to the southwest of China, is a region of high plateau (mostly above 3,700m (12,000ft)) and high mountains: Mount Everest is on its Southern border. Tibet has very cold, frosty winters and warm, rainy summers. For most of the year, crisp, sunny weather prevails but temperatures can fall very low at night. 🔲 Take light to medium clothing in the summer supplemented by much warmer clothes for the cold mountain nights. Heavy clothing is a necessity in the winter.

Lhasa - Tibet
Alt: 3,650m (12,000ft)

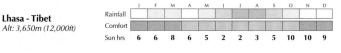

	J	F	M	A	M	J	J	A	S	O	N	D
Rainfall												
Comfort												
Sun hrs	6	6	8	6	5	2	2	3	5	10	10	9

Climate

Tropical Monsoon	
Steppe	
Desert with Cool Season	
Subtropical	
Continental	
High Mountain & Plateau	

Cold but tolerable	Hot but tolerable	Danger of Heatstroke	
Extremely Cold	Comfortable, Temperate	Hot & Sticky, Very Hot	**Key to Comfort**

China - continued

Northwestern China

Xinjiang and the northwestern interior of China is predominantly desert and has very hot summers and bitterly cold winters made even more severe by icy winds. Rainfall is light. Inner Mongolia, which lies to the north and east, has a similar climate but both summer and winter temperatures are lower and winter and spring can bring harsh winds which turn the semi-desert region into a dustbowl.  Take warm clothes even in the summer and much heavier attire in the winter. Also be aware that rainfall, although light, can occur at any time of year.

Colombia

Capital City: **Bogota**　World Map ref: **C4**

This is a large country: it is twice the size of France and has a varied topography and climate to match. It contains part of the Andes mountain chain and has two coasts - one bordering the Pacific Ocean, the other the Caribbean Sea - as well as forested lowlands which form part of the Amazon Basin. On the Pacific Coast and the lower Western slopes of the Andes, you should go prepared for downpours at any time of year. The good news is that most of the rain tumbles down at night but the bad news is that there are frequent afternoon thunderstorms and the overnight downpours do little to refresh the atmosphere which is hot and muggy throughout the year. The Caribbean coast is drier from December to March but be prepared for rain and humid conditions in the wet season which stretches from April to November. Most of the country's interior is mountainous and temperatures drop lower the higher up you go: the tallest peaks are covered in snow for much of the year. In the middle altitudes (where you'll find Bogota), conditions are pleasant and temperate. Here you'll find a climate of perpetual spring where days are warm but never too hot and nights, although cool, are never cold and frosty. However, even here you won't escape the rain: it falls at any time of the year but is heavier on the western ranges than in the east. Prepare for even more rain if you visit the equatorial lowlands of the Amazon Basin. For visits to the coast of Colombia, pack light cotton clothing. For the mountains, pack warm to heavy clothing depending on how high up you are planning to go, and be prepared for rain!

Climate　　**Tropical Equatorial**

Tropical Wet & Dry

High Mountain & Plateau

Bogota Alt: 2,640m (8,700ft)		J	F	M	A	M	J	J	A	S	O	N	D
	Rainfall												
	Comfort												
	Sun hrs	6	5	4	3	3	4	4	4	4	3	4	5

Comoros

Capital City: **Moroni**　World Map ref: **G5**　(In southern hemisphere)

These Indian ocean islands have a warm, tropical climate and their coasts can get very hot and sticky from December to March. On higher ground, temperatures are fresher but heavy rain is always a possibility. Rainfall is substantial all year round but particularly between December and April when there are occasional cyclones. Take light clothes for the summer months (our winter) with warmer cover-ups for their winter if planning a trip to the mountains. Pack a light raincoat whenever you go.

Moroni Alt: 6m (20ft)		J	F	M	A	M	J	J	A	S	O	N	D
	Rainfall												
	Comfort												
	Sun hrs	6	6	7	6	7	8	8	7	7	8	8	7

Climate　　**Tropical Oceanic**

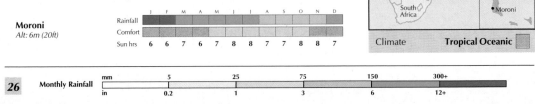

Monthly Rainfall	mm		5		25		75		150		300+
	in		0.2		1		3		6		12+	

Congo – Democratic Republic of Congo *see under* **Zaire**

Congo – Republic of Congo

Capital City: **Brazzaville** World Map ref: **F5**

Northern Congo is rainier than the south and the coastal areas which have a dry season from June to September. Further north, heavy rains fall from January to May and again from October to December. Throughout the year, both temperatures and humidity can be high in Congo. 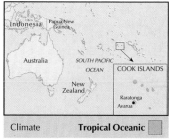 Light clothing made from natural fibres is recommended together with light rainwear in the wet season.

Brazzaville
Alt: 320m (1,050ft)

	J	F	M	A	M	J	J	A	S	O	N	D
Rainfall												
Comfort												
Sun hrs	5	5	5	6	5	5	4	5	4	5	5	5

Climate   **Tropical Equatorial**

Tropical Wet & Dry

Cook Islands

Capital City: **Avarua** World Map ref: **A5** (In southern hemisphere)

Mountainous Raratonga is the best known of the Cook Islands which are a group of six large and myriad smaller Polynesian islands which share a tropical climate, strongly influenced by the seas which surround them. Rain occurs throughout the year but is heaviest between November and April when occasional storms and cyclones can hit. Temperatures and humidity are high all year but May to October are cooler months and even very hot, sticky days are tempered by sea breezes which create a pleasant and healthy climate. 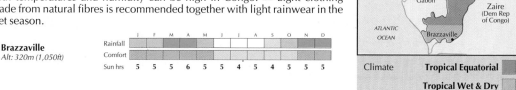 Take light clothing whatever the time of year, supplemented by wraps for cooler evenings. Always go prepared for rain.

Rarotonga
Alt: 7m (25ft)

	J	F	M	A	M	J	J	A	S	O	N	D
Rainfall												
Comfort												
Sun hrs	6	6	6	6	5	5	6	6	6	6	6	6

Climate   **Tropical Oceanic**

Corfu *see under* **Greece**   **Corsica** *see under* **France**

Costa Rica

Capital City: **San José** World Map ref: **B4**

This small, mountainous country lies between Nicaragua and Panama and shares many elements of its climate with the latter. Temperatures are high throughout the year, especially on the Pacific and Caribbean coasts which experience some rain all year and get very wet and sticky indeed during the May to November rainy season. If you prefer more temperate conditions, head for the hills where the air is crisper and the nights are cooler. 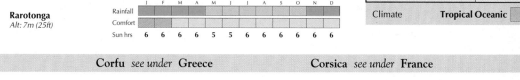 Pack light clothing with warmer clothes for the chilly highland nights and a light raincoat for the rainy season.

San José
Alt: 1,145m (3,800ft)

	J	F	M	A	M	J	J	A	S	O	N	D
Rainfall												
Comfort												
Sun hrs	7	8	8	7	5	4	4	4	5	4	5	6

Climate   **Tropical Wet & Dry**

Crete *see under* **Greece**

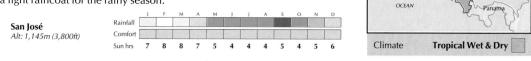

Cold but tolerable	Hot but tolerable	Danger of Heatstroke	Key to Comfort
Extremely Cold	Comfortable, Temperate	Hot & Sticky, Very Hot	

Croatia

Capital City: **Zagreb** World Map ref: **F2**

Croatia's Dalmatian coast is one of the best known tourist regions of the former Yugoslavia. It has a pleasant Mediterranean-type climate of sunny, hot summers (occasionally interrupted by thunderstorms) and largely mild, wet winters although icy winds from central Europe can gust in and make life unpleasant. Inland, and to the East, conditions are more extreme although rainfall is lower than on the coast. In the mountain areas, winters can be bitterly cold with heavy and long-lying snow. ◼ Take light clothing if you are visiting the coast, backed up by a few warmer items for cool nights. Much warmer clothing and rainwear is needed for travelling in the winter.

Climate   **Mediterranean** ▢

             Continental ▢

Dubrovnik
Alt: 50m (160ft)

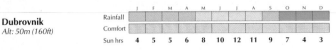

	J	F	M	A	M	J	J	A	S	O	N	D
Rainfall												
Comfort												
Sun hrs	4	5	5	6	8	10	12	11	9	7	4	3

Cuba

Capital City: **Havana** World Map ref: **C3**

Cuba, the largest island in the Caribbean, is only slightly smaller than England. It has a tropical climate and a single rainy season from May to October. The heaviest rainfall takes place on the low-lying north coast of the island and in the hills of the interior. The driest region is in the southeast. Tropical storms and hurricanes can appear between July and November. Winter temperatures in the west sometimes drop below 10°C (50°F), for short spells, as a result of cooler continental air blowing down from North America. Cuba is hot all year but temperatures are never extreme and, even at their hottest, conditions are bearable because sea breezes help dissipate humidity, although nights can be sticky. ◼ Light cotton clothing is appropriate but warmer cover-ups are advisable for winter visits.

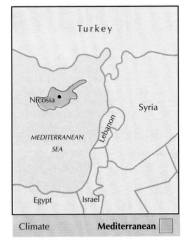

Havana
Alt: 25m (80ft)

Climate   **Tropical Oceanic** ▢

	J	F	M	A	M	J	J	A	S	O	N	D
Rainfall												
Comfort												
Sun hrs	6	6	7	7	8	6	6	6	5	5	5	5

Cyprus

Capital City: **Nicosia** World Map ref: **F3**

No wonder Cyprus is so popular with sun lovers since it enjoys consistently sunny weather from May to September when you will hardly see a cloud in the sky. In the spring and autumn, however, the weather is more mixed and sudden storms are possible, although they rarely last long. Winter brings some rain and falls of snow in the Troodos Mountains. However, even in the winter, Cyprus is a warm and sunny island, clocking up six hours of sunshine a day. The only negative for winter holidaymakers is that the seas around the island are a trifle chilly from December to early May. Those who love bright sunshine but hate extreme heat are advised to visit in spring, before temperatures climb too high. In the summer, nights can be very hot and sticky on the coast although daytime temperatures are moderated by sea breezes. The mountains are delightful in summer: sunny but cooler than on lower ground. ◼ Take beachwear and light clothes for a summer visit with a wrap for chillier evenings inland. Warmer clothes are needed for the winter with heavier attire if you plan to visit the mountains.

Nicosia
Alt: 175m (570ft)

	J	F	M	A	M	J	J	A	S	O	N	D
Rainfall												
Comfort												
Sun hrs	5	7	7	9	11	13	13	12	11	9	7	5

Climate   **Mediterranean** ▢

mm		5		25		75		150		300+

in		0.2		1		3		6		12+

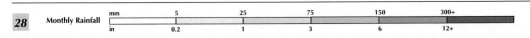

Czech Republic

Capital City: **Prague** World Map ref: **F2**

The Czech Republic, which was part of Czechoslovakia until 1993, is a hilly, landlocked state lying in Central Europe. Its central position brings a mixed climate influenced both by the mild, wet weather of Atlantic Europe and the hot summers and icy winters of Russia. As a result, summers are warm but rainy and prone to disturbances blowing in from the northern Mediterranean. Winters are cold and wet, particularly on high ground where heavy snows linger for up to four months. An occasional spell of settled winter weather can bring a run of cold but crisp, bright days. However, life gets hard when easterly winds howl in from Russia bringing severe cold snaps.

 Wrap up very warmly for a winter visit and supplement lighter clothing with warm cover-ups even in summer. Rainwear is advisable throughout the year but especially in the summer months.

Climate   **Continental**

Prague
Alt: 260m (850ft)

	J	F	M	A	M	J	J	A	S	O	N	D
Rainfall												
Comfort												
Sun hrs	2	3	5	6	8	9	8	8	6	4	2	1

Denmark

Capital City: **Copenhagen** World Map ref: **F2**

Expect British-style weather in Denmark: warm but rainy summers, chilly winters and mild, wet autumns and springs. Winters are often colder than in the UK, however, and the waters of the Baltic can freeze for long periods. Such freezes are not an annual occurrence but, when they do happen, they are accompanied by snow which can lie for as long as a month. February tends to be the coldest time of the year. The climate varies little throughout Denmark although the west coast is rather more prone to rain than the east. The west can also fall prey to strong gales from the Atlantic, so take windproof clothing if visiting this region in winter.  Light clothing is fine for the summer months when the country receives an average of 8 hours of sunshine every day. However, take at least one woolly to combat sudden changes in the weather and, as in Britain, expect the odd short sharp shower.

Climate   **Maritime**

Copenhagen
Alt: 9m (30ft)

	J	F	M	A	M	J	J	A	S	O	N	D
Rainfall												
Comfort												
Sun hrs	1	2	4	5	8	8	8	7	5	3	1	1

Djibouti

Capital City: **Djibouti** World Map ref: **G4**

This small country, which lies at the entrance to the Red Sea, is short on rainfall and high on heat. What coastal rain there is falls between November and March while, inland, Djibouti's extensive plains attract occasional downpours during the summer months from April to October.

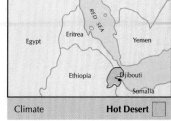 Djibouti basks in a daily average of 9 hours sunshine all year round so take light clothing suitable for the long, sunny days.

Djibouti
Alt: 13m (45ft)

	J	F	M	A	M	J	J	A	S	O	N	D
Rainfall												
Comfort												
Sun hrs	8	8	9	9	10	8	8	9	9	10	10	8

Climate   **Hot Desert**

| Extremely Cold | Cold but tolerable | Comfortable, Temperate | Hot but tolerable | Hot & Sticky, Very Hot | Danger of Heatstroke | **Key to Comfort** |

Dominica

Capital City: **Roseau**   World Map ref: **C4**

Dominica lies at the north end of the Windward Islands and has a mountainous central ridge with tropical rainforest. Its main rainy season is from June to December but showers can occur at any time and there is a possibility of hurricanes between July and November. As on other Caribbean Islands, temperatures are high throughout the year but never extreme. Even during the hottest months, sea breezes counter the effects of heat and humidity although it can get sticky at night. ◧ Light cotton clothing is appropriate for any time of the year along with cover-ups for the occasional chilly winter evening.

Roseau
Alt: 20m (65ft)

	J	F	M	A	M	J	J	A	S	O	N	D
Rainfall												
Comfort												
Sun hrs	8	8	9	8	8	7	8	8	8	7	8	8

Climate	**Tropical Oceanic**

Dominican Republic

Capital City: **Santo Domingo**   World Map ref: **C4**

The Dominican Republic covers the eastern two thirds of the island of Hispaniola, bordering Haiti on the west. Hispaniola is the most mountainous island in the Caribbean and its higher peaks, which soar up to 3,000m (10,000ft), are much cooler and rainier than its lowland areas. Its north coast is wetter than the south and has a higher rainfall than most Caribbean islands during the May to October rainy season when hurricanes sometimes occur. Temperatures are high throughout the year but rarely unbearable because sea breezes help dissipate humidity, although nights can be sticky. ◧ Light cotton clothing is appropriate for any time of the year.

Santo Domingo
Alt: 14m (45ft)

	J	F	M	A	M	J	J	A	S	O	N	D
Rainfall												
Comfort												
Sun hrs	6	6	7	7	6	6	6	7	7	6	6	6

Climate	**Tropical Equatorial**
	Tropical Oceanic

Ecuador

Capital City: **Quito**   World Map ref: **C5**

As its name suggests, Ecuador lies on the Equator. It has a varied topography in which a narrow, low-lying coastal plain rises steeply to a mountainous interior. The forested lowlands to its east form part of the Amazon Basin. These elements give it a climate as varied as its terrain. On the coast, temperatures and humidity are high throughout the year and you should go prepared for downpours during the December to April rainy season. Rain is heavier towards the north, falling off the further south you go along the coastline. Up in the Andes, temperatures drop the higher up you go and the tallest peaks are covered in snow for much of the year. In the middle altitudes, conditions are pleasant and spring-like: days are warm but never too hot and nights, although cool, are never cold and frosty. However, go prepared for rain, which falls largely between September and May, arriving mainly in the afternoon and evening. Prepare for even more rain if you plan to visit the equatorial lowlands of the Amazon Basin which are hot, muggy and wet all year. ◧ Pack light cotton clothing for visits to the coast and warmer to heavy wear for mountain trips.

Quito
Alt: 2,880m (9,400ft)

	J	F	M	A	M	J	J	A	S	O	N	D
Rainfall												
Comfort												
Sun hrs	5	5	4	5	5	6	7	7	8	5	6	6

Climate	**Tropical Equatorial**
	Tropical Oceanic
	High Mountain & Plateau

	mm	5	25	75	150	300+
	in	0.2	1	3	6	12+

The Galapagos Islands

The Galapagos Islands, famed for their astonishing range of wildlife, are also worth visiting if you hate wet weather. The islands are much drier than Ecuador, experiencing light rainfall between January and April. They are also sunny and hot with sea breezes dissipating humidity. 🕶 Light clothes are fine with a wrap to combat sea breezes.

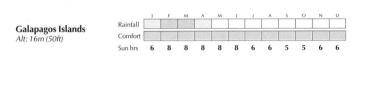

Galapagos Islands		J	F	M	A	M	J	J	A	S	O	N	D
Alt: 16m (50ft)	Rainfall												
	Comfort												
	Sun hrs	6	8	8	8	8	8	6	6	5	5	6	6

Egypt

Capital City: **Cairo** World Map ref: **F3**

Egypt's popularity as a holiday destination stems not only from its ancient heritage but also from its climate. With vast tracts of the country lying actually inside the Sahara, it is one of the world's sunniest environments throughout the year. Cairo averages 11 hours of sunshine a day in the peak summer and 8 hours in the winter. An exception to the sunny norm is Egypt's Mediterranean coast where the winters (November to March), although warm, can bring cloudy days and short periods of rain. More testing, on the coast and in the Nile Delta, are the spring months (March to May) when the Khamsin desert winds can blow strongly and send temperatures soaring making life unpleasant. 🕶 A combination of light and warm clothing is most appropriate for Egypt where very hot daytime temperatures plunge dramatically after sundown.

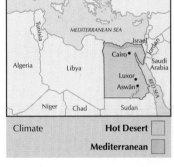

Climate **Hot Desert**

Mediterranean

Cairo		J	F	M	A	M	J	J	A	S	O	N	D
Alt: 65m (210ft)	Rainfall												
	Comfort												
	Sun hrs	7	8	9	10	10	12	12	11	10	9	8	6

El Salvador

Capital City: **San Salvador** World Map ref: **B4**

This tiny country has only one coastline, which lies on the Pacific, and this is its hottest, wettest and most humid region with a heavy rainy season between May and October. There is little rain for the rest of the year. Cooler, crisper conditions are to be found up in the mountains but temperatures everywhere are high throughout the year. 🕶 Take light cotton clothing for the coast, warmer attire if you are planning a trip to the mountains (which can be chilly after sundown) and go prepared for the rainy season.

San Salvador		J	F	M	A	M	J	J	A	S	O	N	D
Alt: 685m (2,250ft)	Rainfall												
	Comfort												
	Sun hrs	10	10	10	8	8	6	8	8	6	7	9	10

Climate **Tropical Wet & Dry**

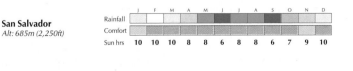

	Cold but tolerable	Hot but tolerable	Danger of Heatstroke	
Extremely Cold		Comfortable, Temperate		Hot & Sticky, Very Hot

Key to Comfort

Equatorial Guinea

Capital City: **Malabo** World Map ref: **F4**

This small country, which borders the Gulf of Guinea, lies to the south of Cameroon and shares its warm, wet climate. Its offshore island, Fernando Po, is particularly rainy because of its mountainous terrain. Rainfall levels are high and rain is possible at any time of the year although less likely during the relatively dry season from December to February. High humidity, high temperatures and much cloud make for an oppressive environment throughout the year. ▣ Keep clothing light and take a good raincoat.

Malabo
Alt: 50m (160ft)

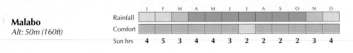

	J	F	M	A	M	J	J	A	S	O	N	D
Rainfall												
Comfort												
Sun hrs	4	5	3	4	4	3	2	2	2	2	3	4

Climate   **Tropical Equatorial**

Eritrea

Capital City: **Asmara** World Map ref: **F4**

Temperatures vary widely here: the coastlands are arid, hot and dry all year but, on the inland plains, the rain falls heavily, especially in July and August, while in December to February you can find yourself shivering in freezing temperatures. ▣ Take light clothing and warm wraps to combat chilly nights inland.

Asmara
Alt: 2,320m (7,600ft)

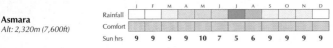

	J	F	M	A	M	J	J	A	S	O	N	D
Rainfall												
Comfort												
Sun hrs	9	9	9	9	10	7	5	6	9	9	9	9

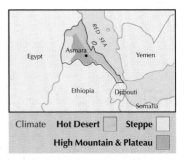

Climate   **Hot Desert** ☐   **Steppe** ☐

High Mountain & Plateau ☐

Estonia *see under* Baltic States

Ethiopia

Capital City: **Addis Ababa** World Map ref: **F4**

A hilly country with high mountain ranges soaring up to 4,600m (15,000ft), Ethiopia has a range of climatic conditions. Its eastern lowland areas are hot and sticky with a desert-like climate, while conditions are more temperate up in the hills and much cooler in the mountains. The country has a heavy rainy season, between June and September, when the central and western highlands will witness downpours. These are more ferocious in the west where up to 2,000mm (80in) of rain falls every year and thunderstorms are frequent. Suggestions on suitable clothing vary according to the region being visited. ▣ Light clothes are best for the hot lowlands but warmer attire is needed in the hills and visitors should wrap up well if going high into the mountains. Night temperatures can be particularly chilly.

Addis Ababa
Alt: 2,410m (7,900ft)

	J	F	M	A	M	J	J	A	S	O	N	D
Rainfall												
Comfort												
Sun hrs	9	9	8	7	8	6	3	3	5	8	9	9

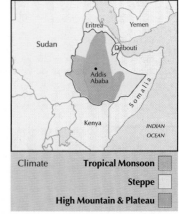

Climate   **Tropical Monsoon** ▣

Steppe ☐

High Mountain & Plateau ▣

mm		5	25	75	150	300+
in		0.2	1	3	6	12+

Falkland Islands

Capital City: **Stanley** World Map ref: **C7** (In southern hemisphere)

The Falkland Islands, which lie around 400 miles off the South American coast, are largely low-lying and cool currents from the Antarctic keep their climate temperate, if rainy. Conditions are similar to those of the Shetland Islands off the coast of Scotland, although winters can be stormier with frequent gales (the Roaring Forties) and snow storms. Summers are cool and very changeable, as in Britain. ▥ It is easy to pack for The Falklands. Just take the kind of clothes you would wear in the UK: light to medium clothes for the summer months (November to March), much warmer clothing in the winter be prepared for rain at all times.

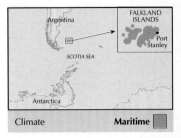

Climate   Maritime

Stanley
Alt: 2m (7ft)

	J	F	M	A	M	J	J	A	S	O	N	D
Rainfall												
Comfort												
Sun hrs	7	6	5	3	2	2	2	3	4	5	7	7

Faroe Islands

Capital City: **Tórshavn** World Map ref: **E1**

Looking at the map, you might expect the weather on these islands to be horrific since they lie right in the middle of the stormy Atlantic Ocean. Fortunately for their inhabitants, the waters which surround them are warmed by the Gulf Stream and this keeps temperatures moderately high, although sunshine is minimal in the summer months and clouds and rain abound. ▥ Take light to warm clothing for the summer and prepare for snow if visiting during the winter months. You are unlikely to need your sunglasses here: a windcheater will probably prove more useful.

Climate   Maritime

Tórshavn
Alt: 50m (160ft)   No weather statistics are available for this location

Fiji

Capital City: **Suva** World Map ref: **J5** (In southern hemisphere)

Fiji has a tropical oceanic climate which means that it experiences plenty of rain of the "liquid sunshine" variety which falls in short, intense bursts interspersed with periods of brilliant sunshine. Temperatures are consistently high throughout the year. Humidity and rainfall are at their highest between November and April although brisk sea breezes generally prevent conditions from becoming unbearably sticky. Suva is on the southeast coast and, thanks to the prevailing trade winds, is wet all year. You may also find more rain, mist and cooler temperatures on higher ground. ▥ Pack light clothing, a wrap for cooler evenings and be prepared for rain whatever the time of year.

Climate   **Tropical Oceanic**

Suva
Alt: 6m (20ft)

	J	F	M	A	M	J	J	A	S	O	N	D
Rainfall												
Comfort												
Sun hrs	7	6	6	7	7	7	7	8	7	7	7	7

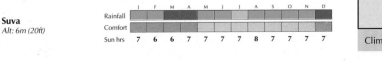

| Extremely Cold | Cold but tolerable | Comfortable, Temperate | Hot but tolerable | Hot & Sticky, Very Hot | Danger of Heatstroke |

Key to Comfort

Finland

Capital City: **Helsinki** World Map ref: **F1**

Finland is a country of extremes with very harsh winters but warm, pleasant summers. The north of the country lies inside the Arctic Circle and this means summer days are not only sunny but long with an average of 10 hours of sunshine. However temperatures tend to be higher in the low-lying south. In winter, central and southern Finland enjoy relatively mild weather while the rest of the country shivers and dons its snowboots. In the north, the winter snows can last up to seven months, so only visit at this time if you're very fond of snowmen. One compensation for the cold winters is that they bring long bouts of settled weather. In the summer, the weather is very changeable and light rain always a possibility.  Take very warm clothing in the winter months, especially if you plan to enter the Arctic Circle. Light to warm clothing is appropriate for the summer and always pack insect repellant: gnats and mosquitoes are a pest, especially in the north.

Helsinki
Alt: 45m (150ft)

	J	F	M	A	M	J	J	A	S	O	N	D
Rainfall												
Comfort												
Sun hrs	1	3	4	6	9	10	9	8	5	3	1	1

Climate   **Continental**

Subarctic

France

Capital City: **Paris** World Map ref: **E2**

This large country has the lot - soaring mountains, beaches, river valleys, wide plains - with a variety of weather conditions to match. In the north and west, you will find a maritime climate with warm to hot summers and cool but mild winters. However rain can be a nuisance at any time of year, so go prepared.

The lower parts of Central and Eastern France suffer colder winters but have warmer summers than the north. Rain falls mainly in the summer and can be accompanied by dramatic storms.

Up in the mountains, the snowy winters are a joy for skiers but heavy autumn rains can make life miserable in the Pyrenees. In the Vosges, Jura and the Northern Alps, summer days can also be rained off. The Southern Alps, the Pyrenees and parts of the Massif Central enjoy sunnier summers interspersed with sudden, and shortlived, bouts of rain and thunder. In the summer, the valleys are sunnier than the mountain tops which are often shrouded in cloud. In winter, it is the other way round.

Sunlovers should head for southwestern France or the Mediterranean coast. Summers in these regions are hot and sunny and winters are mild but be prepared for short but heavy bursts of summer rain and occasional storms. If you are on the Mediterranean coast in spring, brace yourself for the occasional arrival of the Mistral, a cold and blustery wind which disrupts the normally balmy weather.  In most parts of France, you should dress as you would in the UK, basing a summer travel wardrobe around light clothes, supplemented by heavier wear for chilly days and evenings. In the mountains, warm clothing is recommended.

Climate   **Mediterranean**

Maritime   **Continental**

High Mountain & Plateau

Nice
Alt: 4m (13ft)

	J	F	M	A	M	J	J	A	S	O	N	D
Rainfall												
Comfort												
Sun hrs	5	6	6	8	9	10	11	10	8	7	5	5

Paris
Alt: 75m (250ft)

	J	F	M	A	M	J	J	A	S	O	N	D
Rainfall												
Comfort												
Sun hrs	2	3	5	6	7	8	8	7	6	4	2	2

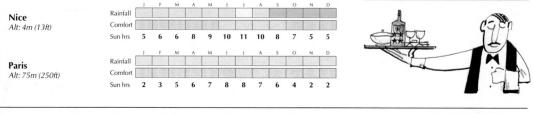

mm		5	25	75	150	300+
in		0.2	1	3	6	12+

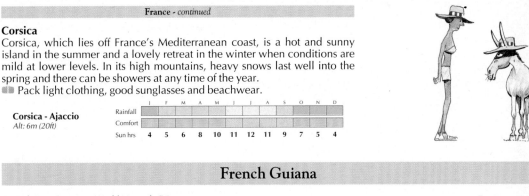

France - *continued*

Corsica

Corsica, which lies off France's Mediterranean coast, is a hot and sunny island in the summer and a lovely retreat in the winter when conditions are mild at lower levels. In its high mountains, heavy snows last well into the spring and there can be showers at any time of the year.
🧳 Pack light clothing, good sunglasses and beachwear.

Corsica - Ajaccio		J	F	M	A	M	J	J	A	S	O	N	D
Alt: 6m (20ft)	Rainfall												
	Comfort												
	Sun hrs	4	5	6	8	10	11	12	11	9	7	5	4

French Guiana

Capital City: **Cayenne**   World Map ref: **D4**

This small country borders Brazil and Surinam and has an Atlantic coastline. It consists largely of lowland plains with small hills to the south and has a Turkish bath-like climate throughout the year, experiencing very heavy rain from December to mid-July. The best time to go is between August and November when conditions are much drier. 🧳 Take very light cotton clothing and reliable waterproofs if you are visiting in the long wet season.

Cayenne		J	F	M	A	M	J	J	A	S	O	N	D
Alt: 8m (25ft)	Rainfall												
	Comfort												
	Sun hrs	5	4	4	4	4	6	7	8	9	9	8	6

Climate   **Tropical Equatorial**

French Polynesia

Capital City: **Papeete**   World Map ref: **A5**   (In southern hemisphere)

French Polynesia comprises the Society Islands (which include Tahiti and the capital Papeete), Tuamotu and the Gambia Islands, the Tabuai chain and the Marquesas Islands. There are two main seasons in these tropical islands: the weather is hot, sticky and wet from November to April while slightly cooler and much drier conditions prevail between May and October. Conditions are kept bearable by strong sea breezes but these can make evenings chilly. 🧳 Take a warm wrap to supplement light clothes worn during the hot days. Pack a light raincoat if you are travelling during the rainy season.

Tahiti		J	F	M	A	M	J	J	A	S	O	N	D
Alt: 90m (300ft)	Rainfall												
	Comfort												
	Sun hrs	5	6	7	7	7	7	7	7	8	7	7	6

Climate   **Tropical Oceanic**

Gabon

Capital City: **Libreville**   World Map ref: **F5**

Gabon, which is sandwiched between Cameroon and Congo, should be visited between June and August when heavy rainfall eases off and humidity levels drop. Even at this time, you'll find the climate hot and sticky with heavy clouds obscuring the sun. 🧳 Light clothing is fine but, outside the dry season, effective waterproofs are a must.

Libreville		J	F	M	A	M	J	J	A	S	O	N	D
Alt: 12m (40ft)	Rainfall												
	Comfort												
	Sun hrs	5	6	5	5	5	4	4	3	3	4	4	5

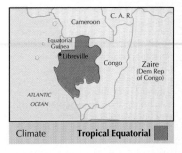

Climate   **Tropical Equatorial**

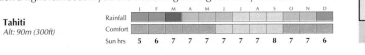

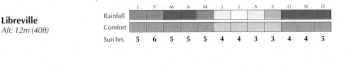

Cold but tolerable	Hot but tolerable	Danger of Heatstroke	
Extremely Cold	Comfortable, Temperate	Hot & Sticky, Very Hot	**Key to Comfort**

Gambia

Capital City: **Banjul** World Map ref: **E4**

Gambia's pleasant winter climate has made it a prime resort for holidaymakers. From November to May, its coastal areas bordering the Gambia River are very sunny and even its rains, which fall between June and October, are of the "liquid sunshine" variety with warm downpours interspersed by sunny periods. During the dry season, temperatures are much higher inland than on the coast but lower at night. Humidity brings some discomfort from June to October. Light clothing is fine for any time of year.

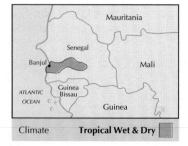

Banjul
Alt: 2m (7ft)

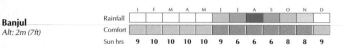

	J	F	M	A	M	J	J	A	S	O	N	D
Rainfall												
Comfort												
Sun hrs	9	10	10	10	10	9	6	6	6	8	8	9

Climate   **Tropical Wet & Dry**

Georgia

Capital City: **Tbilisi** World Map ref: **G2**

Georgian summers are long and hot but very rainy, particularly in the west on the Black Sea coast which has an almost subtropical climate. Winters are dryer and mild but, up in the Caucasus Mountains, temperatures can fall dramatically and heavy snowfalls are likely. Pack light clothes with rainwear for the summer and warmer attire in the winter months and wrap up well if you are planning to visit the mountains.

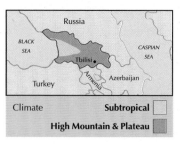

Tbilisi
Alt: 490m (1,600ft)

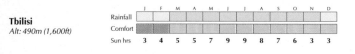

	J	F	M	A	M	J	J	A	S	O	N	D
Rainfall												
Comfort												
Sun hrs	3	4	5	5	7	9	9	8	7	6	3	3

Climate   **Subtropical**

          High Mountain & Plateau

Germany

Capital City: **Berlin** World Map ref: **F2**

Germany has a varied topography with a climate to match. Conditions can alter from day to day, year to year and region to region depending on which direction the weather fronts are coming: the sea or Continental Europe.

The Baltic Coast suffers harsher winters than the North Sea Coast. Baltic summers are warm and sunny but even the brightest summer days can be dramatically interrupted by thunderstorms. The North Sea coast enjoys the mildest winters in the whole of Germany except when the bitter east wind comes out to play. Rains can be heavy here in autumn but rain and storms from the Atlantic are possible at any time of year, so always have waterproofs with you.

Inland, the North German Plain, which houses Hanover and Berlin, shows small differences in weather between the west and east. In winter, the east is more exposed to the bitterly cold winds from Russia which are occasionally harsh enough to freeze canals and rivers. Summers are sunnier and less rainy than on the coasts: rain does occur but showers tend to be short, if intense.

In the central and southern hills, where Liepzig and Munich are situated, summer conditions vary from year to year: a good year brings long spells of sunshine but a bad year plagues inhabitants and visitors with lowering clouds and rain. Winter conditions vary according to altitude: the Bavarian Hills and Hartz Mountains experience long, snowy winters and the valleys surrounding them experience the occasional sharp frost.

Monthly Rainfall

mm		5		25		75		150		300+
in		0.2		1		3		6		12+

Germany - continued

Northern Rhineland is a major wine growing region even though winters can be cold and summers changeable. Overall, summer weather is predominantly warm with a fair amount of sunshine. The Upper Rhine Valley produces tobacco as well as wine, a tribute to its sunny summer climate which makes this region the warmest in Germany. Winters are another matter and can get very chilly but not as chilly as in the Bavarian Alps, Germany's most mountainous area and a centre for wintersports. Winters are crisp and snowy here and summers are fairly warm but very wet.

Combine warmer clothes with lightweights in the summer and be prepared to wrap up well in the winter months. Take a raincoat if you are planning to visit the North Sea coast.

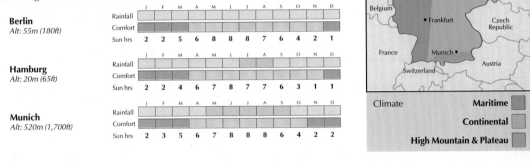

Berlin
Alt: 55m (180ft)

	J	F	M	A	M	J	J	A	S	O	N	D
Rainfall												
Comfort												
Sun hrs	2	2	5	6	8	8	8	7	6	4	2	1

Hamburg
Alt: 20m (65ft)

	J	F	M	A	M	J	J	A	S	O	N	D
Rainfall												
Comfort												
Sun hrs	2	2	4	6	7	8	7	7	6	3	1	1

Munich
Alt: 520m (1,700ft)

	J	F	M	A	M	J	J	A	S	O	N	D
Rainfall												
Comfort												
Sun hrs	2	3	5	6	7	8	8	8	6	4	2	2

Climate — Maritime / Continental / High Mountain & Plateau

Ghana

Capital City: **Accra**   World Map ref: **E4**

Ghana gets more rain inland than on its Gulf of Guinea coastline. In the north, the rains fall from May to September, while the south has two rainy seasons with maximum falls in May/June and again in October. Be prepared for hot, sticky weather as humidity levels are high throughout the year.

Lightweight clothing made from natural fibres is most appropriate with a light raincoat for the rainy months.

Accra
Alt: 65m (210ft)

	J	F	M	A	M	J	J	A	S	O	N	D
Rainfall												
Comfort												
Sun hrs	7	8	7	7	7	5	5	5	6	7	8	8

Climate — Tropical Equatorial / Tropical Wet & Dry

Gibraltar

Capital City: **Gibraltar**   World Map ref: **E3**

Gibraltar is hot and sunny in the summer, clocking up between 10 and 11 hours of sunshine a day but occasional high winds blustering around The Rock can have a chill edge to them. Hardly any rain falls during the peak summer months (June to September) but the climate makes up for it in the winter when storms blowing in from the Atlantic can make life exciting for a day or two. In the summer, pack light clothes with a light jacket or shawl for protection against the wind. Even in the winter, conditions on Gibraltar are mild so you shouldn't need heavy clothing, but be prepared for rain.

Gibraltar
Alt: 5m (16ft)

	J	F	M	A	M	J	J	A	S	O	N	D
Rainfall												
Comfort												
Sun hrs	6	7	7	8	10	11	11	11	9	7	6	6

Climate — Mediterranean

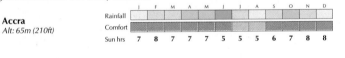

Cold but tolerable	Hot but tolerable	Danger of Heatstroke
Extremely Cold	Comfortable, Temperate	Hot & Sticky, Very Hot

Key to Comfort

Greece

Capital City: **Athens** World Map ref: **F3**

In summertime Greece swelters under cloudless skies, clocking up as many as 12 hours of sunshine a day and, although sea breezes take the edge off the heat in the islands and on the coast, a large conurbation like Athens can be impossibly hot and oppressive.

Those who find extreme heat uncomfortable should visit in the autumn months of September and October when the weather is sunny, resorts relatively uncrowded and the sea deliciously warm. Spring is also pleasant although only the hardy will venture to swim. Winter brings some rain and even snow, although this rarely sticks around for long except in the mountains where conditions can be severely cold. Northern Greece is slightly colder and wetter than the south and, if travelling here, you should brace yourself for sudden thunderstorms even in the height of summer. Light clothing for the summer should be supplemented by a warm cover-up for the occasional chilly evening or blustery day (the northerly Etesian wind, which plays round the islands, can reach gale force at times!) Take warmer clothes on a winter visit, especially if you are going to Northern Greece or into the mountains.

	J	F	M	A	M	J	J	A	S	O	N	D
Athens Rainfall												
Alt: 105m (340ft) Comfort												
Sun hrs	4	5	6	8	9	11	12	12	9	7	5	4

Climate **Mediterranean**

Corfu

Corfu is the principal of the islands which lie in the Ionian Sea, the deepest part of the Mediterranean, and is more sheltered from the wind but experiences more rain than the islands of the Aegean. The winter months here are very rainy indeed; in fact, Corfu is the wettest part of Greece, recording a higher annual rainfall than London! All this rainfall makes the island one of the lushest and most beautiful in Greece. Not for Corfu is the scorched scrubbiness which afflicts other parts of the country after the long summer drought and the island's thick vegetation gives it a sub-tropical feel. Even the winds are gentler here: Corfu does not fall prey to the strong northerly winds which can rage through the Aegean, a mixed blessing since it means that conditions on the island can be more sultry than elsewhere during the heat of the summer. At summer's end, the stickiness increases when the island falls under the sleepy spell of the Sirocco, a warm wind which brings high humidity in its wake and ushers in the beginning of the rains.

Light clothes and beachwear are fine for the summer months but, outside June to August, be prepared for rain.

	J	F	M	A	M	J	J	A	S	O	N	D
Corfu - Corfu Town Rainfall												
Alt: 25m (80ft) Comfort												
Sun hrs	4	5	6	8	10	11	11	11	9	7	4	3

Crete

By far the largest of the Greek islands, Crete has a climate all of its own and weather conditions vary considerably from north to south. Even at the height of summer, the north of the island can be made chilly by the Aegean winds which can blow up to gale force and bring clouds in their wake. The great spine of mountains which dominates the centre of the island attracts cloud and some light rain in the summer and snow and frost in the winter. However, the island's south, which lies almost at the southernmost tip of Europe, is blessed with wonderful weather and experiences long spells of cloudless sunshine in the summer and high temperatures even in the winter months. Light clothes are fine in the summer, supplemented by slightly warmer attire in the autumn and winter. Further north, take warm cover-ups against the wind and if visiting the mountains.

Monthly Rainfall	mm		5		25		75		150		300+	
	in		0.2		1		3		6		12+	

Greece - *continued*

Crete - Heraklion Alt: 40m (130ft)		J	F	M	A	M	J	J	A	S	O	N	D
	Rainfall												
	Comfort												
	Sun hrs	3	5	6	8	10	12	13	12	10	6	6	4

Rhodes

Rhodes, the gateway to the Dodecanese islands in the southeast corner of the Aegean, claims to be the sunniest of the Greek islands and its "summer season" extends well into October. The sea stays warm enough to swim in until early November but winter, when it comes, is sharp, bringing a rapid rise in winds and fall in temperature. Although the climate is still fairly mild in the winter, the strong winds bring a chill to the air and, even in the height of summer, their ferocity can be annoying to beach-bound holidaymakers, although they do make this one of the most popular Greek islands for sailors.  Light clothing with a windcheater for blustery days is fine in the summer months. Take warmer clothing if you are travelling later in the year or in early spring.

Greenland

Capital City: **Godthåb**   World Map ref: **D1**

Greenland is the world's largest island and, since three quarters of it lies within the Arctic Circle, winters are long and very ferocious while summers get shorter the further north you go. Northern Greenland, and most of the country's interior, consists of a 3,000m (10,000 ft) deep ice cap and has a truly Arctic climate with temperatures rarely rising above freezing point, even in the short summer. The country's coasts have long, snowy winters and cool, short but drier summers and there can be pleasant summer days when the sun is strong and the wind is weak. The coasts and the southern mountains behind are the only parts of Greenland free of permanent snow and ice. Glaciers in these mountains produce most of the icebergs in the North Atlantic. 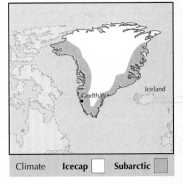 Don't even think of going to Greenland unless you've stocked up with thermals, windproofs, waterproofs and layers of warm to heavy clothing. Some lighter clothes, sunglasses and sunscreen should be packed for a summer visit.

Godthåb Alt: 50m (160ft)		J	F	M	A	M	J	J	A	S	O	N	D
	Rainfall												
	Comfort												
	Sun hrs	1	3	6	8	6	5	6	4	3	2	1	0

Climate   **Icecap** ☐   **Subarctic** ▨

Grenada

Capital City: **St George's**   World Map ref: **C4**

Grenada is the southernmost of the Windward Islands. A large, mountainous island, it attracts more rain than is normal in the Caribbean. This falls mainly from June to December and can intensify during the July to November hurricane season when tropical storms occasionally make life difficult, even if they don't hit the island directly. As in the rest of the Caribbean, summer is hotter than winter but temperatures are high throughout the year. The heat is rarely unbearable because sea breezes help dissipate the humidity although nights can be sticky.  Light cotton clothing and a light raincoat is needed whatever the time of year, and take cover-ups for winter evenings.

St George's Alt: 6m (20ft)		J	F	M	A	M	J	J	A	S	O	N	D
	Rainfall												
	Comfort												
	Sun hrs	9	8	7	8	8	7	8	8	8	8	8	8

Climate   **Tropical Oceanic** ▨

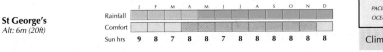

Cold but tolerable		Hot but tolerable		Danger of Heatstroke	
Extremely Cold		Comfortable, Temperate		Hot & Sticky, Very Hot	

Key to Comfort

Guadeloupe

Capital City: **Basse-Terre** World Map ref: **C4**

The French-owned islands of Guadeloupe are the southernmost of the Leeward Islands. The main rainy season here is from June to November but showers can occur at any time of the year. The rainfall statistics are for Camp Jacob and reflect the much heavier rains that occur throughout the year in the mountainous interior. Hurricanes can hit the islands between July and November. Temperatures are high throughout the year and high humidity can make life a sticky business during the rainy season, in particular, although nights are cooler than days. ▦ Pack light cotton clothing with warmer cover-ups for inland areas and winter evenings. Also go prepared for rain, whatever the time of year.

Camp Jacob
Alt: 530m (1,750ft)

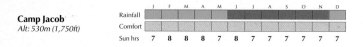

	J	F	M	A	M	J	J	A	S	O	N	D
Sun hrs	7	8	8	8	7	8	7	7	7	7	7	7

Climate **Tropical Oceanic**

Guatemala

Capital City: **Guatemala City** World Map ref: **B4**

One of the larger central American countries, Guatemala is renowned for its archaelogical sites and frequent earthquakes. It has a short Caribbean and a much longer Pacific coastline and both these regions are hot, humid and wet in the May to October rainy season. Temperatures also soar in the northern plains which can be rainy at any time of year but are wettest between May and September. To the west and south lie high plateau and mountains. The capital, Guatemala City, is located on this high ground and, subsequently, has a pleasant climate with cooler temperatures and a dry season from November to April. ▦ Take light clothes if you are visiting the coasts, warmer cover-ups for the highlands and a raincoat in the wet season.

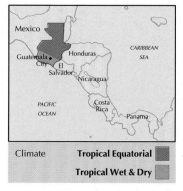

Guatemala City
Alt: 1,480m (4,900ft)

	J	F	M	A	M	J	J	A	S	O	N	D
Sun hrs	5	5	5	4	3	1	2	1	2	2	3	5

Climate **Tropical Equatorial**
 Tropical Wet & Dry

Guinea

Capital City: **Conakry** World Map ref: **E4**

Guinea has a tropical climate with very high rainfall during its May to November rainy season. Downpours reach their peak in July, August and September and are particularly heavy on the Atlantic coast where there is little sunshine to be seen during the wet months. Humidity levels are high all year round but, when the rains tail off in early November, the country enjoys a period of hot, bright weather which lasts until April. ▦ Light clothing is fine from November to April but waterproofs are essential during the rainy season.

Conakry
Alt: 50m (160ft)

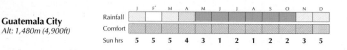

	J	F	M	A	M	J	J	A	S	O	N	D
Sun hrs	5	7	9	7	5	3	2	2	4	5	6	3

Climate **Tropical Monsoon**

mm	5	25	75	150	300+
in	0.2	1	3	6	12+

Guinea-Bissau

Capital City: **Bissau**   World Map ref: **E4**

This tiny country borders Guinea to the south and shares its tropical climate. It has a very heavy rainy season from May to November when conditions are made unpleasant by high humidity. Things look up between December and April when Harmattan desert winds bring dryer air to the interior and trade winds perk up the coast. Dry season temperatures get higher the further you go inland but tend to plummet at night. Take light clothing and good waterproofs for the rains and warmer attire for dry season nights inland.

Bissau
Alt: 40m (130ft)

	J	F	M	A	M	J	J	A	S	O	N	D
Rainfall												
Comfort												
Sun hrs	8	9	10	10	9	7	5	4	5	7	8	8

Climate   **Tropical Monsoon**

Guyana

Capital City: **Georgetown**   World Map ref: **D4**

This country, which is about the size of Britain, borders Brazil, Venezuela and Surinam and has an Atlantic coastline. It has an Equatorial climate which is warm, wet and humid all year with heavy rains twice a year (May to July and November to January). You can gain some relief from the sticky heat and rain by moving to higher ground inland where rain is lighter and falls mainly between April and September. Pack light cotton clothing and waterproofs, with a warm cover-up if you are visiting the highland region.

Georgetown
Alt: 2m (7ft)

	J	F	M	A	M	J	J	A	S	O	N	D
Rainfall												
Comfort												
Sun hrs	6	7	7	7	6	6	7	8	8	7	7	6

Climate   **Tropical Equatorial**

Haiti

Capital City: **Port-au-Prince**   World Map ref: **C4**

Haiti occupies the western third of Hispaniola, a large and mountainous Caribbean island which also holds the Dominican Republic. Rain falls throughout the year on Haiti but its north coast and mountainous interior are wetter than the south. Temperatures are always high but humidity on the coast is rather lower than elsewhere in the Caribbean. The air is fresher and cooler in the mountains. Pack light cotton clothing and a light raincoat for any time of the year. Take warmer clothes if you are planning a trip to the mountains.

Port-au-Prince
Alt: 30m (100ft)

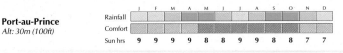

	J	F	M	A	M	J	J	A	S	O	N	D
Rainfall												
Comfort												
Sun hrs	9	9	9	9	8	8	9	9	8	8	7	7

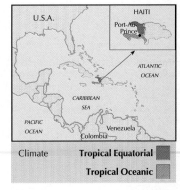

Climate   **Tropical Equatorial**

Tropical Oceanic

Hawaiian Islands *see under* **United States**

Cold but tolerable   Hot but tolerable   Danger of Heatstroke

Extremely Cold   **Comfortable, Temperate**   **Hot & Sticky, Very Hot**

Key to Comfort

Honduras

Capital City: **Tegucigalpa** World Map ref: **B4**

Similar in size to its neighbour Guatemala, Honduras has a short Pacific coast and a much longer Caribbean coastline with an area of low-lying plain to the east and a mountainous interior. Both coasts are hot and humid. The Caribbean coast (unusually for Central America) receives most of its rainfall during the winter months but can also be affected by the tail end of a hurricane between June and November. Temperatures are high in the eastern plains but, up in the mountains, conditions are cooler and pleasant with moderate rain in the summer months (May to October). 🔳 Take light clothes with warmer cover-ups for the highlands plus rainwear if you are visiting the coastal regions.

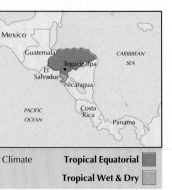

Tegucigalpa
Alt: 1,005m (3,300ft)

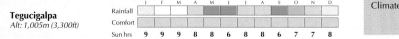

	J	F	M	A	M	J	J	A	S	O	N	D
Rainfall												
Comfort												
Sun hrs	9	9	9	8	8	6	8	8	6	7	7	8

Climate   **Tropical Equatorial**

Tropical Wet & Dry

Hong Kong

Capital City: **Victoria - Hong Kong City** World Map ref: **I3**

Hong Kong lies on the border of the tropics and has a monsoon climate with a heavy rainy season stretching from May to September. The climate is predominantly dry and pleasant from mid-October to March although the spring months, February to April, are sometimes cloudy and overcast. Summers can be very clammy and hot as well as rainy and you should be wary of visiting between July and September when typhoons, blowing in from the South China Sea, can wreak havoc. 🔳 Take light clothing plus a light raincoat in the summer, backed up by warmer clothes for protection against chilly evenings and fierce air-conditioning. Take fairly warm clothes if you are planning a winter trip.

Hong Kong
Alt: 35m (110ft)

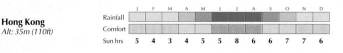

	J	F	M	A	M	J	J	A	S	O	N	D
Rainfall												
Comfort												
Sun hrs	5	4	3	4	5	5	8	6	6	7	7	6

Climate   **Tropical Monsoon**

Hungary

Capital City: **Budapest** World Map ref: **F2**

Buried deep in Central Europe, far from the influence of the sea, Hungary has a settled climate with hot summers and cold, snowy winters. Spring and early summer are the most unsettled periods of the year when temperatures can rise or fall sharply from day to day, rain is heavy, and there are frequent thunderstorms. Summers are generally sunny and hot but sudden rain showers can occur at any time of the year. 🔳 Light clothing is suitable for the summer months. In autumn and spring, prepare to be adaptable with a combination of light and warm clothing plus rainwear. Take warm clothes, a scarf and sturdy boots to combat the winter snows, fog and icy winds.

Budapest
Alt: 140m (460ft)

	J	F	M	A	M	J	J	A	S	O	N	D
Rainfall												
Comfort												
Sun hrs	2	3	5	7	8	9	10	9	7	5	2	1

Climate   **Continental**

Ibiza see under **Spain**

	mm	5	25	75	150	300+
Monthly Rainfall	in	0.2	1	3	6	12+

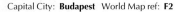

Iceland

Capital City: **Reykjavik**   World Map ref: **E1**

One enduring memory of Iceland is of watching elderly folk swimming up and down a hot pool in Reykjavik while flakes of snow descended gently through the steam above their heads. Another is of battling to ride an Icelandic pony across an icy plain while a bitter wind howled around our miserable heads. In this country, you can have fun but it is almost always in spite of the weather; not surprising when you consider that Iceland lies at the heart of the Atlantic's stormiest region. The warm Gulf Stream keeps winters mild on lower ground but, since the island lies right in the path of Atlantic depressions, its weather is even more changeable than ours. Be prepared for anything here: a day can start sunny, turn drizzly, revert back to brilliant sunshine and end with snow. Your best bet is to layer up with light clothing which can be supplemented with woollens. Take heavier clothes for the winter, and always go prepared for rain.

Climate   Subarctic

Reykjavik		J	F	M	A	M	J	J	A	S	O	N	D
Alt: 14m (45ft)	Rainfall												
	Comfort												
	Sun hrs	1	2	4	5	6	6	6	5	4	2	1	0

India

Capital City: **Delhi**   World Map ref: **G3-H3**

Expect a hot, tropical climate when visiting India with variations from region to region. If you like temperate conditions, go in the winter when evenings and mornings are cool and crisp and days dry and sunny. Between April and June, in the run-up to the monsoon season, conditions can be insufferably hot and dusty. June to September is the monsoon season when you should brace yourself for heavy rain. However, this should only be taken as a broad guide to a country where local conditions differ greatly from place to place.

Northern & North Eastern India
In the Himalayas, winter conditions are cold and wet with heavy snow while mid-summer is unpleasantly hot. Here, you should take a mixture of light and warm clothing for a summer visit but pack heavy clothes for winter.
On the northern plains of India, extending from the Punjab in the west to Calcutta in the east, you'll find a climate of extremes. To the east, hot and thundery summer weather between March and June is followed by a very oppressive monsoon season when extremely high humidity makes life unpleasant. To the west, (Rajasthan) and northwest of Delhi, desert conditions prevail and summers are drier. The winter months (December to February) bring crisp, sunny weather by day but nights are chilly. For a summer visit, take light clothing and if travelling in the east of this region go prepared for the monsoon rains. Pack warm clothes for the winter months.
The best time to visit the extreme northeast of India (Assam) is late autumn or spring. At these times, the weather is warm, dry and sunny. For the entire summer, Assam is a washout, literally, with tumultuous rains making life unbearable. Take light clothes for the daytime, warmer attire for the evenings and, if you must go in the summer, good waterproofs!

Climate   **Tropical Equatorial**
                 Tropical Monsoon
Hot Desert   **Steppe**
                 Subtropical
High Mountain & Plateau

Calcutta		J	F	M	A	M	J	J	A	S	O	N	D
Alt: 5m (16ft)	Rainfall												
	Comfort												
	Sun hrs	8	9	9	9	8	5	4	4	5	7	8	8

Delhi		J	F	M	A	M	J	J	A	S	O	N	D
Alt: 220m (720ft)	Rainfall												
	Comfort												
	Sun hrs	7	9	8	9	8	6	6	6	7	9	10	9

World Climate Map
see pages 6-7

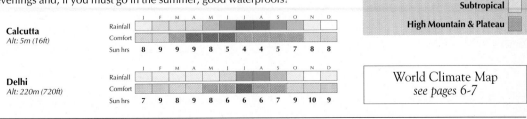

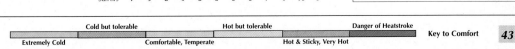

Cold but tolerable	Hot but tolerable	Danger of Heatstroke
Extremely Cold	Comfortable, Temperate	Hot & Sticky, Very Hot

Key to Comfort

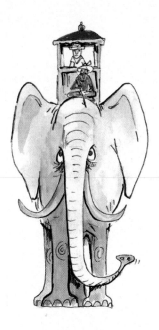

India - *continued*

Central & Southern India

On India's central plateau, temperatures are slightly lower and conditions are, therefore, more pleasant during the hot season. However, the monsoon rains can be intense. ▆ Light clothes are fine for daytime wear, whatever the time of year, but you will need warmer attire for colder nights and go prepared for the monsoon season.

The west coast of India, which includes Bombay and Goa, consists of a narrow coastal plain rising to steep mountains, the Western Ghats. During the winter and spring (November to April) daytime temperatures are warm and sunny and humidity is at its lowest. In the hot season, conditions can be unbearable unless you go way up into the hills and very heavy monsoon rains fall from June to September. In the southwest, the big rains come earlier and summers are cooler than in the north. High humidity can make conditions stifling except on the coast where the stickiness is dissipated by sea breezes. ▆ Supplement light clothes with warmer wraps, especially in the winter, and waterproofs for the monsoon rains.

The southeast of India receives its rains in the late autumn, from October to December, and has hot, muggy weather throughout the year. The only relief is to be found in the cooler hill region but, here, winter temperatures can fall very low and warm clothing is recommended.

Bombay
Alt: 10m (35ft)

	J	F	M	A	M	J	J	A	S	O	N	D
Rainfall												
Comfort												
Sun hrs	9	10	9	10	10	5	2	3	5	8	9	9

Goa
Alt: 60m (200ft)

	J	F	M	A	M	J	J	A	S	O	N	D
Rainfall												
Comfort												
Sun hrs	9	10	9	10	10	5	2	3	5	8	9	9

Indonesia

Capital City: **Jakarta**   World Map ref: **I5** (In southern hemisphere)

Indonesia, which comprises over 13,500 islands, as well as the western part of New Guinea, has a tropical climate but conditions vary greatly from area to area. The larger islands, of which the best known are Sumatra, Java, Bali, Lombok and Borneo, are mountainous and volcanic with colder, rainy conditions prevalent in their upper reaches. In the lowlands, conditions are equatorial: warm, steamy and wet. Rain falls throughout the year and intensity varies from region to region depending on whether it is brought by the north monsoon (November to March) or the south monsoon (May to September). Parts of Indonesia are the most thundery places in the world so this is not a place to make for if you're scared of storms! That said, Indonesia is popular with the holiday trade because its rainy periods are interspersed with spells of bright, sunny weather: Bali has lashings of sunshine throughout the year. Temperatures and humidity are high on the coast where conditions can feel muggy and oppressive although sea breezes make life more tolerable. Inland conditions are cooler, especially on higher ground and at night. ▆ Take light clothes and be prepared for rain whatever the time of year. Pack warmer attire if you are travelling away from the coast.

Climate   **Tropical Equatorial** ▆
              Tropical Monsoon ▆

Bali
Alt: 10m (35ft)

	J	F	M	A	M	J	J	A	S	O	N	D
Rainfall												
Comfort												
Sun hrs	8	10	10	10	9	9	9	10	11	10	10	10

Jakarta
Alt: 8m (25ft)

	J	F	M	A	M	J	J	A	S	O	N	D
Rainfall												
Comfort												
Sun hrs	5	5	6	7	7	7	7	8	8	7	6	5

Weather Statistics for 315 locations around the world *see pages 94-103*

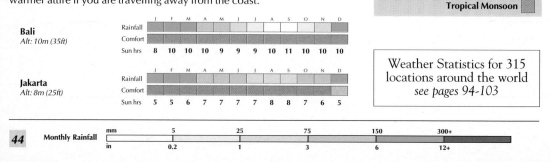

mm		5		25		75		150		300+
in		0.2		1		3		6		12+	

Iran

Capital City: **Tehran** World Map ref: **G3**

Iran is a huge country whose vast central plains are surrounded by mountains. The plains experience extreme conditions in both the summer and winter. In the summer, searing hot, dry, almost desert-like conditions prevail while the winter months bring changeable weather which can vary from mild and muggy to icy cold, when the harsh Siberian winds sweep through. The best place to be in the winter is along the coast of the Persian Gulf or on the shore of the Arabian Sea where conditions are milder. In the summer, however, temperatures here can soar as high as on the plains and are exacerbated by high humidity creating a risk of heatstroke for the unwary. The most temperate part of Iran is the small region of forest which borders the Caspian Coast. This receives the highest level of rainfall in the country. In the rest of Iran, winter and spring are the rainiest periods. ▥ Take light, loose clothing with head covers for the summer months, wrap up much more warmly in the winter and anticipate rain in the winter and spring. Women should respect the Islamic dress code.

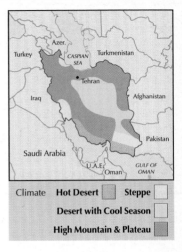

Climate   **Hot Desert** ▨   **Steppe** ☐

Desert with Cool Season ☐

High Mountain & Plateau ▨

Tehran
Alt: 1,205m (4,000ft)

	J	F	M	A	M	J	J	A	S	O	N	D
Rainfall												
Comfort												
Sun hrs	6	7	7	7	9	12	11	11	10	8	7	6

Iraq

Capital City: **Baghdad** World Map ref: **G3**

Most of Iraq consists of flat lowland desert and river valleys, although there are mountains in the northeast (Kurdistan) and a short coastline on the Persian Gulf. The desert region records some of the world's highest temperatures in the summer. When the Shamal wind blows hot and dusty to make life even more trying, there is the danger of heat exhaustion or even heatstroke. Winters are mild in the south of Iraq but grow colder the further north you go and Kurdistan has heavy snows. ▥ Take very light, loose clothing on a summer visit, medium to warm clothes for the winter months and even warmer clothing for the mountains.

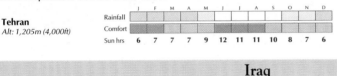

Climate   **Hot Desert** ▨   **Steppe** ☐

High Mountain & Plateau ▨

Baghdad
Alt: 35m (110ft)

	J	F	M	A	M	J	J	A	S	O	N	D
Rainfall												
Comfort												
Sun hrs	6	7	8	9	10	12	11	11	11	9	7	6

Ireland

Capital City: **Dublin** World Map ref: **E2**

Irish women are famed for their dewy complexions thanks largely to the soft rain which falls on their country all year round. If you hate getting wet, head for Dublin or Cork in the east and south where the climate is somewhat drier, or time your Irish trip for May when the weather is warmest and sunniest. The west coast is stunningly beautiful but you will spend some of your time peering at the magnificent coastline and the Atlantic breakers through a fog of cloud and mist. In winter, the west falls prey to some ferocious storms while the whole of Ireland, in common with mainland UK, can occasionally be afflicted by cold spells when northerly and easterly winds bring snow and frost. ▥ Light clothes supplemented with warmer jackets are fine during the summer; wrap up more warmly in the winter months. Always take an umbrella - but think how good all that drizzle is for the skin!

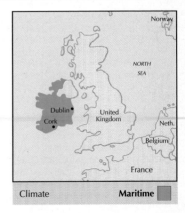

Dublin
Alt: 50m (160ft)

	J	F	M	A	M	J	J	A	S	O	N	D
Rainfall												
Comfort												
Sun hrs	2	3	3	5	6	6	5	5	4	3	2	2

Climate   **Maritime** ▨

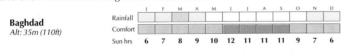

Cold but tolerable		Hot but tolerable		Danger of Heatstroke
Extremely Cold	Comfortable, Temperate		Hot & Sticky, Very Hot	

Key to Comfort

Israel

Capital City: Jerusalem World Map ref: **F3**

More than half of Israel is desert and there are pronounced differences in the climate between the Negev desert region and the fertile north of the country. In the North, a Mediterranean climate prevails bringing hot, dry summers and mild, wet winters. Frost and snow are virtually unheard of but winter rain comes in short, intense bursts, so be prepared. On the coast, the summer weather is muggier and afternoons, when sea breezes disperse some of the humidity, are the most pleasant times of the day. In the inland hills around Galilee, summer daytime conditions are dryer and more pleasant but nights can be chilly and winter brings both heavy rainfall and occasional snowfalls. Beyond the hills to the south lies the desert where rainfall is low and localised, taking the form of sudden, intense showers during the winter months. Daytime summer conditions here can be very hot, especially when the warm Khamsin (or, in Hebrew, "Sharav") wind blows but nights are chilly and crisp. Israel is a very sunny country with up to 7 hours of sun a day in the winter and up to 13 in the summer. This has made it a popular holiday destination throughout the year but an especially good option for winter sun.
 Pack light clothing for the summer with warmer cover-ups for winter visits, the hills of Galilee and nights in the desert. Include a light scarf in early summer to protect yourself from the dusty Khamsin winds.

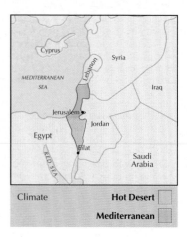

Climate

| Hot Desert | |
| Mediterranean | |

Eilat
Alt: 12m (40ft)

	J	F	M	A	M	J	J	A	S	O	N	D
Rainfall												
Comfort												
Sun hrs	7	8	8	9	10	11	11	11	10	9	8	7

Jerusalem
Alt: 760m (2,500ft)

	J	F	M	A	M	J	J	A	S	O	N	D
Rainfall												
Comfort												
Sun hrs	6	7	7	10	11	14	13	13	11	7	7	6

Italy

Capital City: Rome World Map ref: **F2**

What you should pack for an Italian odyssey depends on which part of the country you are visiting, and when. In the Italian Alps, the high peaks attract snow in the winter and rain in the summer months. Lower down in the valleys, both summer and winter temperatures are higher: the lakeland district around Lakes Maggiore, Como and Garda is delightfully warm and sunny in the summer months while winters are mild.  Take light clothes supplemented by a few warmer cover-ups in the summer but wrap up more warmly in winter.

In the Po Valley and the North Italian Plain, which stretch from Turin to Venice, summers are very hot and sunny but winters can be gloomy indeed. If you are heading for the area around Trieste, icy winds from central Europe can gust in and make life very unpleasant. Pack light clothes for summer but in winter anticipate fog, frost or snow and dress accordingly.

The coast of southern Italy is the prime spot for sunworshippers, who bask in its Mediterranean summers. In the "leg" of Italy, which stretches from Genoa in the north to Brindisi in the south, you'll find quite a difference in climate between the sunny coast and the mountainous interior: while the Apennines are chilly and wet in summer and cloaked in snow during the winter months, coastal winters are mild, particularly in the rainier west. The sunniest, driest weather in Italy is enjoyed by the inhabitants of its southernmost "toe". For a trip to the coast, pack light summer clothing with warm cover-ups to combat sea breezes. Medium clothing is fine for winters on the coast but wrap up well if going to the mountains.

Monthly Rainfall	mm	5	25	75	150	300+
	in	0.2	1	3	6	12+

Italy - *continued*

The east of Italy, although drier, can be afflicted by strong winds. Outside the summer months, expect the unexpected on the Italian Peninsula: spring, autumn and winter weather can be very quirky, alternating between mild sunny days and spells of heavy cloud and rain. 🏳 Take light clothing for a summer visit and warmer clothing for winter.

Rome
Alt: 20m (65ft)

	J	F	M	A	M	J	J	A	S	O	N	D
Rainfall												
Comfort												
Sun hrs	4	4	6	7	8	9	11	10	8	6	4	4

Venice
Alt: 2m (7ft)

	J	F	M	A	M	J	J	A	S	O	N	D
Rainfall												
Comfort												
Sun hrs	3	4	5	6	8	9	10	8	7	5	2	3

Sardinia

Sardinia lies west of the Italian mainland and enjoys sunny, dry weather throughout the year. Even in winter, it basks in up to 4 hours of sunshine a day while summer brings 10 to 11 hours of daily sun. This can mean warm, sticky nights if you are staying on the coast, but daily sea breezes temper the mid-day heat. 🏳 Take light clothing in the summer with a warmish cover-up for the evenings. Mix in warmer clothes for a winter visit.

Sardinia - Cagliari
Alt: 4m (13ft)

	J	F	M	A	M	J	J	A	S	O	N	D
Rainfall												
Comfort												
Sun hrs	4	4	6	7	9	9	11	10	8	6	4	3

Sicily

Sicily, the largest Mediterranean island, lies off the southern tip of Italy and is dry and sunny. In winter, it attracts up to 6 hours of sunshine a day while the summer brings 10 to 11 hours. The high temperatures can mean warm, sticky summer nights but daily sea breezes moderate the mid-day heat.
🏳 Take light clothes with a jacket or shawl in the summer and add medium weight clothing for a winter visit.

Sicily - Palermo
Alt: 25m (80ft)

	J	F	M	A	M	J	J	A	S	O	N	D
Rainfall												
Comfort												
Sun hrs	4	5	6	7	8	10	10	9	8	6	6	4

Climate	
Mediterranean	
Continental	
High Mountain & Plateau	

Weather Statistics for 315
locations around the world
see pages 94-103

Ivory Coast

Capital City: **Yamoussoukro** World Map ref: **E4**

The south of the Ivory Coast is sandwiched between Liberia and Ghana. In the south and along the coast, there are two rainy seasons - March to July and October to December - with torrential downpours during the first rains. Humidity is high throughout the year and rain can occur along the coast at any time. Inland and in the north, there is one rainy season from May to September and a long dry season throughout the winter months.
🏳 Light clothing is appropriate with waterproofs for the rains and warmer clothing for winter evenings which can be chilly.

Abidjan
Alt: 7m (25ft)

	J	F	M	A	M	J	J	A	S	O	N	D
Rainfall												
Comfort												
Sun hrs	6	7	7	7	6	4	4	4	4	6	7	7

Climate	
Tropical Equatorial	
Tropical Wet & Dry	

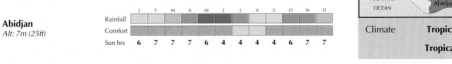

Cold but tolerable		Hot but tolerable		Danger of Heatstroke	
Extremely Cold	**Comfortable, Temperate**		**Hot & Sticky, Very Hot**		

Key to Comfort

Jamaica

Capital City: **Kingston** World Map ref: **C4**

This large, mountainous tropical island lies to the south of Cuba and west of Haiti. Its Blue Mountains tower up to 2,700m (7,500 ft) and their northern slopes get substantial rainfall all year. Kingston's sheltered south coast and the popular tourist resorts of the north coast are much drier. Most rain falls between May and October and there is the risk of a passing hurricane during the latter part of this period. Temperatures are consistently hot with an average of 8 hours of daily sunshine throughout the year and sea breezes help to counter the effects of heat and humidity.  Take light clothing of natural fibre to keep your cool in the moist heat, and take warmer cover-ups for the winter evenings and trips to higher ground.

Kingston
Alt: 35m (110ft)

	J	F	M	A	M	J	J	A	S	O	N	D
Rainfall												
Comfort												
Sun hrs	8	9	9	9	8	8	9	8	8	7	8	8

Climate   **Tropical Oceanic**

Japan

Capital City: **Tokyo** World Map ref: **I3**

Japan, a group of mountainous volcanic islands off the coast of Asia, has a predominantly temperate, seasonal climate with cool to cold but sunny winters, warm to hot summers and mild weather in the spring and autumn. However, there are exceptions to this: the island of Hokkaido and the northern areas of Honshu experience heavy snows in the winter months when cold winds gust in from Siberia gathering moisture from the sea as they come. In central and southern Japan, winter is the (relatively) dry season while there is moderate rainfall in the summer and autumn with the chance of a typhoon, accompanied by heavy rainfall, blowing in from the South China Sea from July to September. Southern summers tend to be warm and humid with heavy cloud cover. The mountain areas are usually the most pleasant parts of Japan in the summer months when conditions are predominantly sunny and crisp. The best time to visit the lower parts of the country is in the springtime when you'll find fresh, sunny weather and the legendary cherry blossom. 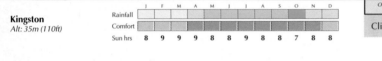 While light clothes are fine in the summer, you should combine light clothing with some warmer attire in the spring and autumn, and take much warmer clothing for the winter and visits to the mountain areas. Go prepared for rain in the summer.

Sapporo
Alt: 20m (65ft)

	J	F	M	A	M	J	J	A	S	O	N	D
Rainfall												
Comfort												
Sun hrs	3	4	5	7	7	7	6	6	6	5	4	3

Tokyo
Alt: 5m (16ft)

	J	F	M	A	M	J	J	A	S	O	N	D
Rainfall												
Comfort												
Sun hrs	6	6	6	7	6	5	6	7	5	4	5	5

Climate   **Subtropical**

Continental

Jordan

Capital City: **Amman** World Map ref: **F3**

All but 10 per cent of Jordan is desert which means that the country has predominantly long, dry, hot summers with chilly nights and cold, crisp winters. Rain in the desert regions is sparse, falling in short, intense bursts

World Climate Map
see pages 6-7

Monthly Rainfall

mm	5	25	75	150	300+
in	0.2	1	3	6	12+

Jordan - *continued*

during the winter and spring. The most fertile part of Jordan is the hilly region in the northwest which experiences high rainfall between November and March when weather fronts blow in from the Mediterranean. To the west of the hills lies the long valley where the River Jordan flows into the Dead Sea which is 400m (1,300ft) below sea level. This valley has very hot summers, warm winters and little rain. Expect sun throughout the year in Jordan: the country clocks up as many as 13 hours of sunshine a day in the summer and up to 7 hours a day in winter.  In the summer, light clothing is fine but take a warm wrap for protection against chilly desert evenings. Pack warmer clothing and be prepared for rain if visiting the northwest in the winter months.

Amman
Alt: 770m (2,500ft)

	J	F	M	A	M	J	J	A	S	O	N	D
Rainfall												
Comfort												
Sun hrs	7	7	8	10	11	13	13	13	11	10	8	6

Climate   **Hot Desert** □   **Steppe** □

Kazakhstan

Capital City: **Alma-Ata**   World Map ref: **G2**

This large country lies in the driest part of the former Soviet Union and is a land of desert and plains. Summers can be extremely hot although low humidity prevents conditions from becoming unbearable. Sunshine levels are high throughout the year, averaging 4 hours a day in the winter and 9 to 10 in the summer but winters are very cold unless you head for the shores of the Caspian Sea where conditions are milder.  Take light clothing in the summer and warm to heavy clothing for the winter months. Rainfall is generally low but can occur at any time of the year, so be prepared.

Alma-Ata
Alt: 775m (2,550ft)

	J	F	M	A	M	J	J	A	S	O	N	D
Rainfall												
Comfort												
Sun hrs	4	4	5	7	8	9	10	10	8	6	4	4

Climate   **Steppe** □

Desert with Cool Season □

Continental ■

High Mountain & Plateau ■

Kenya

Capital City: **Nairobi**   World Map ref: **F5**

Not surprisingly, for one of the world's top holiday destinations, Kenya has (on the whole) a delightful climate. Sunworshippers staying in hotels along its Indian Ocean coast are saved from overheating by cool sea breezes; its hilly regions have seasonal changes but are always temperate and even its lowlands avoid the plague of high humidity: thanks to coastal breezes they are hot but dry.

Weather conditions vary from region to region. The coast has two rainy seasons: heavy rains fall during April and May with lighter precipitation in October and November. There can be showers at any time of year but these, conveniently, take place largely at night. Nights can be sultry but days are fresher with an average of 8 hours of sunshine and sea breezes to counter humidity.  Light clothes are recommended here with wraps for protection against chilly morning breezes.

Inland from the coast, in the lowlands, the weather is drier and hotter and desert-like towards the northern frontier. Because humidity is low, the heat is rarely oppressive but it is a good idea to acclimatise before rushing about in it.  Take light clothing.

Cold but tolerable		Hot but tolerable		Danger of Heatstroke	**Key to Comfort**
Extremely Cold	**Comfortable, Temperate**		**Hot & Sticky, Very Hot**		

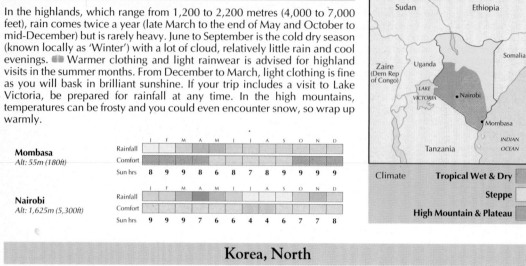

Kenya - continued

In the highlands, which range from 1,200 to 2,200 metres (4,000 to 7,000 feet), rain comes twice a year (late March to the end of May and October to mid-December) but is rarely heavy. June to September is the cold dry season (known locally as 'Winter') with a lot of cloud, relatively little rain and cool evenings. Warmer clothing and light rainwear is advised for highland visits in the summer months. From December to March, light clothing is fine as you will bask in brilliant sunshine. If your trip includes a visit to Lake Victoria, be prepared for rainfall at any time. In the high mountains, temperatures can be frosty and you could even encounter snow, so wrap up warmly.

Mombasa
Alt: 55m (180ft)

	J	F	M	A	M	J	J	A	S	O	N	D
Rainfall												
Comfort												
Sun hrs	8	9	9	8	6	8	7	8	9	9	9	9

Nairobi
Alt: 1,625m (5,300ft)

	J	F	M	A	M	J	J	A	S	O	N	D
Rainfall												
Comfort												
Sun hrs	9	9	9	7	6	6	4	4	6	7	7	8

Climate

Tropical Wet & Dry	
Steppe	
High Mountain & Plateau	

Korea, North

Capital City: **Pyongyang**   World Map ref: **I3**

North Korea has a wide coastal plain in the West rising to mountains in the interior and north and its long border with Manchuria brings it ill winds from China and Siberia which exacerbate its already harsh winters. Snow falls heavily and temperatures are icy enough to freeze rivers for up to four months! July to August are the hottest, most humid and rainiest months. Rainfall is possible at any time of year but tends to tail off in the spring and autumn when temperatures are mild. Take light clothing and a raincoat in the summer, fairly warm attire in the spring and autumn and Dr Zhivago-style gear to face the winter.

Pyongyang
Alt: 30m (100ft)

	J	F	M	A	M	J	J	A	S	O	N	D
Rainfall												
Comfort												
Sun hrs	6	7	7	8	8	7	6	7	7	8	6	6

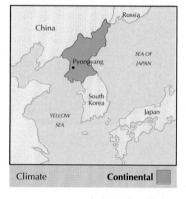

Climate   **Continental**

Korea, South

Capital City: **Seoul**   World Map ref: **I3**

South Korea occupies the southern end of a mountainous peninsular and experiences very cold winters for its latitude. The harshest winter conditions prevail from December to February. Spring and autumn months are mild and fairly dry while summers are hot and very rainy, particularly in July and August. Rain can fall at any time of year. In the summer, take light clothing and a raincoat, put in warmer clothes for spring and autumn trips and pack very heavy clothes for the winter months when icy winds can send temperatures plunging well below freezing point.

Seoul
Alt: 85m (280ft)

	J	F	M	A	M	J	J	A	S	O	N	D
Rainfall												
Comfort												
Sun hrs	6	7	7	8	8	7	6	7	7	8	6	6

Climate   **Subtropical**

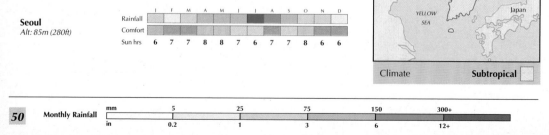

mm	5	25	75	150	300+
in	0.2	1	3	6	12+

Kuwait

Capital City: **Kuwait** World Map ref: **G3**

Imagine a European pattern of weather with much more sun and much less rain and you have the winter weather of Kuwait. However, this low-lying desert country has very hot summers which, although humid, are rainless. No wonder air-conditioning is so popular here: there are times when scorching winds blow in straight from Arabia to make the already difficult heat well nigh unbearable. Occasionally, these hot winds whip up sandstorms; not a good time to be out of doors. Temperatures are a little lower on the Persian Gulf coast but humidity is higher so you are not much better off. The best bet for those who can't function in extreme heat is to go in the winter or spring when temperatures are much more moderate and can even get a bit chilly when northerly winds usher in cold air from Iraq. What rain there is falls between November and March but is light and very sporadic. 🚪 Take very light, loose clothes for the summer with slightly warmer gear in the winter months. Pack a warm cover-up to combat that fierce air-conditioning!

Climate   **Hot Desert**

Kuwait
Alt: 5m (16ft)

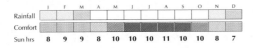

	J	F	M	A	M	J	J	A	S	O	N	D
Rainfall												
Comfort												
Sun hrs	8	9	9	8	10	10	10	11	10	10	8	7

Kyrgyzstan

Capital City: **Bishkek** World Map ref: **G2**

You'll find bright sunshine in Kyrgyzstan for more than two-thirds of the year. Although it is a mountainous region with all year snows in its upper reaches, the country lies a long way from the sea and, as a result, rainfall is low. Even in the valleys, winters are intensely cold but relatively short. Summers are hot and dry with lower temperatures in the mountains. 🚪 In the summer, you will need warm clothes for the evenings and, in winter, go prepared for high mountain conditions.

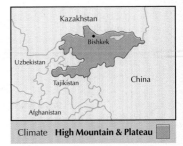

Bishkek
Alt: 760m (2,500ft)

No weather statistics are available for this location

Climate   **High Mountain & Plateau**

Laos

Capital City: **Vientiane** World Map ref: **I4**

Laos is a hilly, landlocked country with jungle covering more than 60 per cent of its surface. It has a single rainy season (May to October) and a dry, sunny climate, averaging 8 hours of daily sunshine for the rest of the year. The best time to visit Laos is during the winter months when the humidity, which makes the rainy season such a trial, abates. 🚪 In low-lying areas, light clothing is fine, whatever the time of year, but be prepared for the monsoon rains. Winter conditions are chillier up in the mountains, especially when cloudy fronts blow in from China, so take warmer clothing if you are planning to go high up.

Climate   **Tropical Monsoon**

Vientiane
Alt: 170m (560ft)

	J	F	M	A	M	J	J	A	S	O	N	D
Rainfall												
Comfort												
Sun hrs	8	8	7	8	7	5	5	5	8	8	8	8

Latvia *see under* **Baltic States**

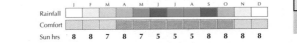

	Cold but tolerable		Hot but tolerable		Danger of Heatstroke	
Extremely Cold		Comfortable, Temperate		Hot & Sticky, Very Hot		

Key to Comfort

Lebanon

Capital City: Beirut World Map ref: **F3**

This tiny land, which is not much larger than an English shire, has two mountain ranges and a remarkably varied climate. On its coast, summers are hot and muggy, while autumn and winter can bring prolonged periods of cloud and rain interspersed with bright spells. Inland, along the narrow Bekaa Valley, summers are hotter and dryer and winters cooler than on the coast, with less rainfall. Up in the mountains, summers are delightfully sunny and crisp and winter snows lie for many months so, in the spring, it is possible to ski one day and sunbathe on the balmy Mediterranean coast the next (the Lebanese say you can do both in a day but you'd need an extremely fast car or, preferably, a helicopter!). The best times to visit are in the spring and autumn when the weather is warm and sunny but humidity is not too high, although the hot Khamsin winds can sometimes make life unpleasant for a day or two. ▇▇ Light clothes are fine in the summer unless you are going into the mountains. Take warmer clothing and be prepared for rain in the winter months.

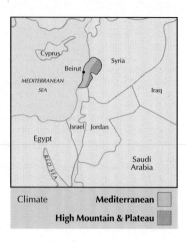

Climate   **Mediterranean** ▢

High Mountain & Plateau ▨

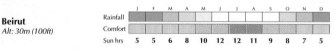

Beirut
Alt: 30m (100ft)

	J	F	M	A	M	J	J	A	S	O	N	D
Rainfall												
Comfort												
Sun hrs	5	5	6	8	10	12	12	11	9	8	7	5

Lesotho

Capital City: Maseru World Map ref: **F6** (In southern hemisphere)

Lesotho contains the highest land in Southern Africa and, in its upper reaches, temperatures can be very low with snow appearing between May and September. The heaviest rainfall arrives between October and April; January/February are the hottest as well as the wettest months. Night temperatures can be chilly at any time of year. ▇▇ Combine warm clothes with lightweights and go prepared for the rainy season.

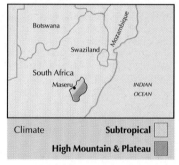

Climate   **Subtropical** ▢

High Mountain & Plateau ▨

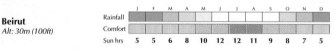

Maseru
Alt: 1,630m (5,300ft)

	J	F	M	A	M	J	J	A	S	O	N	D
Rainfall												
Comfort												
Sun hrs	9	9	8	8	8	8	8	9	9	9	9	10

Liberia

Capital City: Monrovia World Map ref: **E4**

The good news about Liberia is that temperatures vary little throughout the year so light clothes in natural fabrics are always a safe bet. The bad news is that, although hot, the weather is horribly humid, particularly on the coast, and incredibly wet from May to November. The stickiness is somewhat alleviated from December to March by the arrival of the Harmattan winds although these can be dusty and choking. ▇▇ Take light clothing and good waterproofs for the rains. Pack scarves to protect against the Harmattan in late winter.

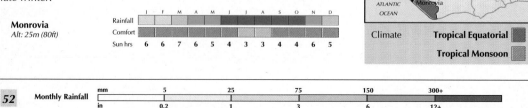

Climate   **Tropical Equatorial** ▨

Tropical Monsoon ▨

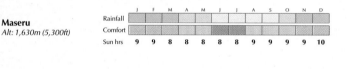

Monrovia
Alt: 25m (80ft)

	J	F	M	A	M	J	J	A	S	O	N	D
Rainfall												
Comfort												
Sun hrs	6	6	7	6	5	4	3	3	4	4	6	5

mm	5	25	75	150	300+
in	0.2	1	3	6	12+

Libya

Capital City: **Tripoli**   World Map ref: **F3**

Libya is a blend of searing desert heat and Mediterranean balminess. About 100 miles inland from the country's Mediterranean coast lies the central Sahara where some of the highest temperatures on earth have been recorded. Between March and June, visitors to the more temperate Libyan coast should brace themselves for a visit from the desert in the shape of hot dusty Sirocco winds which send temperatures soaring and make life unpleasant for a short while. Those going into the desert should also prepare for cold nights. From October to March, the Libyan coast can attract clouds and rain but the heaviest rainfall is in the hilly region of Jebel Akhdar. ▦ Pack light clothes for the coast, supplemented with scarves if you are travelling during sirocco season. Take warm clothing for visiting the desert regions at night.

Climate   **Hot Desert**
              Mediterranean

Tripoli
Alt: 20m (65ft)

	J	F	M	A	M	J	J	A	S	O	N	D
Rainfall												
Comfort												
Sun hrs	5	6	6	7	8	10	11	11	8	7	5	5

Liechtenstein

Capital City: **Vaduz**   World Map ref: **E2**

This tiny principality, which nestles in the central Alps between Austria and Switzerland, has a temperate but very rainy climate. Summers are warm but frequently showery, while winter temperatures range from cool to cold and frosty. ▦ Even in the summer, you should supplement light clothes with warmer attire. Go prepared for rain at any time of the year and wrap up warmly against those cold winters.

Vaduz
Alt: 460m (1,500ft)

	J	F	M	A	M	J	J	A	S	O	N	D
Rainfall												
Comfort												
Sun hrs	2	3	5	6	7	7	8	7	6	3	2	1

Climate   **High Mountain & Plateau**

Lithuania *see under* **Baltic States**

Luxembourg

Capital City: **Luxembourg**   World Map ref: **E2**

Although only a tiny land, no larger than an English shire, Luxembourg, which lies between Belgium and France, manages to encompass a wide range of climatic conditions. Its north, which lies in the densely wooded hills of the Ardennes, is wetter than the south whose eastern part lies in the balmy Moselle Valley. Here, summers are warm to hot and autumns mild enough to allow the cultivation of grapes for wine making. Winters, however, can be very cold on occasion. ▦ Take British-style clothing for most of the year, supplemented by warmer attire in the winter months. Anticipate rain at any time of year.

Luxembourg
Alt: 330m (1,100ft)

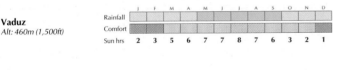

	J	F	M	A	M	J	J	A	S	O	N	D
Rainfall												
Comfort												
Sun hrs	1	2	5	6	6	6	6	5	3	1	1

Climate   **Maritime**

	Cold but tolerable		Hot but tolerable		Danger of Heatstroke	Key to Comfort
Extremely Cold		Comfortable, Temperate		Hot & Sticky, Very Hot		

Macao

Capital City: Macao World Map ref: **I3**

Macao has a tropical climate which gives it hot, very rainy summers and mild to warm winters. Temperatures can climb into the low 30s Centigrade (high 80s Fahrenheit) between June and September when very high humidity can make conditions steamy. Typhoons have been known to strike during this period. 🔹 In the summer months, take light clothing and go prepared for rain. The lowest winter temperatures can drop to 10°C (50°F) in January and February so supplement light clothes with warmer cover-ups at this time of year.

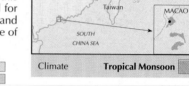

Macao
Alt: 55m (180ft)

	J	F	M	A	M	J	J	A	S	O	N	D
Rainfall												
Comfort												
Sun hrs	5	3	3	3	5	6	8	7	6	7	6	6

Climate   **Tropical Monsoon**

Macedonia *see under* **Yugoslavia**

Madagascar

Capital City: Antananarivo World Map ref: **G5** (In southern hemisphere)

My most enduring memory of Madagascar is of driving through lush cane fields with a cloudless blue sky to the right and purple-black churning storm clouds looming like a mountain to the left. A ferocious storm soon followed but passed almost as quickly as it arrived leaving brilliant sunshine in its wake. On this island, be prepared for anything. Vast beaches, high mountains, extinct volcanoes - it's got the lot, and a mixture of tropical weather to match. Thanks to the trade winds, the east coast has heavy rain all year but the rainy season for the central plateau and the rest of the island is from November to March. The western and southern lowlands are drier and warmer. In fact, warm temperatures prevail except in the mountains. 🔹 Take light clothes with warmer attire for evenings and mountain visits.

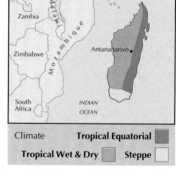

Antananarivo
Alt: 1,375m (4,500ft)

	J	F	M	A	M	J	J	A	S	O	N	D
Rainfall												
Comfort												
Sun hrs	7	8	7	8	7	7	7	7	9	9	8	6

Climate   **Tropical Equatorial**

Tropical Wet & Dry   **Steppe**

Madeira *see under* **Portugal**   **Majorca** *see under* **Spain**

Malawi

Capital City: Lilongwe World Map ref: **F5** (In southern hemisphere)

The weather is healthy and pleasant in Malawi provided you avoid the southern lowlands of the Shire Valley where extreme heat and very high humidity are the order of the day - and nights. Conditions around Lake Malawi are delightful with hot sunshine tempered by cool breezes. The rainy season is from November to March although the mountain areas are very wet indeed with the heaviest rains occurring a little later, in March and April. 🔹 Light clothing is perfect for the Lake Malawi region with warm clothing if you plan a trip to the mountains.

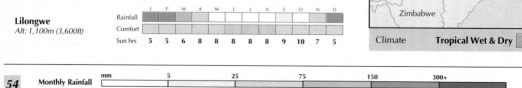

Lilongwe
Alt: 1,100m (3,600ft)

	J	F	M	A	M	J	J	A	S	O	N	D
Rainfall												
Comfort												
Sun hrs	5	5	6	8	8	8	8	8	9	10	7	5

Climate   **Tropical Wet & Dry**

---

mm		5	25	75	150	300+
in		0.2	1	3	6	12+

Malaysia

Capital City: **Kuala Lumpur**   World Map ref: **H4**

Malaysia, which comprises the Malay Peninsular, Sarawak and Sabah, has an equatorial climate and 75 per cent of its land area is tropical rainforest. This makes it hot, steamy and wet throughout the year with much of its rainfall accompanied by thunderstorms. The southwest (April to September) and northeast (November to February) monsoon winds do much to disperse the sticky heat and alternate to produce a double rainy season. The heaviest rain is at the time of changeover of monsoon winds around March to April and October. The coasts exposed to the northwest monsoon tend to be wetter than those exposed to the southwest monsoon, and rainfall across the country varies according to the prevailing monsoon winds. Slightly cooler weather is to be found up in the hills but this is often marred by heavy cloud and high humidity. Take light clothes with slightly warmer clothing if going to the hill regions, and go prepared for rain at any time of the year.

| | Climate | **Tropical Equatorial** |

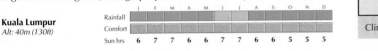

Kuala Lumpur
Alt: 40m (130ft)

	J	F	M	A	M	J	J	A	S	O	N	D
Rainfall												
Comfort												
Sun hrs	6	7	7	6	6	7	7	6	6	5	5	5

Maldives

Capital City: **Male**   World Map ref: **G4**

There are 1,200 of these lovely islands clustered in the North Indian Ocean but only 200 are inhabited and some are mere stretches of coral reef. All have a hot, tropical climate with substantial rainfall during the southwest monsoon which strikes between May and November. Swimming and snorkelling are at their best between December and April when rainfall is at its lowest. Take very light clothes - temperatures and humidity are high throughout the year.

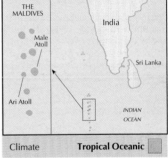

| | Climate | **Tropical Oceanic** |

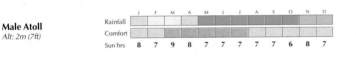

Male Atoll
Alt: 2m (7ft)

	J	F	M	A	M	J	J	A	S	O	N	D
Rainfall												
Comfort												
Sun hrs	8	7	9	8	7	7	7	7	7	6	8	7

Mali

Capital City: **Bamako**   World Map ref: **E4**

Most of Mali's population is based in the south which lies in the Sahel region. The northern half of the country lies in the Sahara desert. During the winter months, the south of the country sees scarcely a drop of rain but, from May to October, it's a different story. The rainy season reaches a crescendo in July and August when there are heavy downpours, mainly in the afternoons and early evenings. These are often accompanied by storms. Rainfall decreases the further north you go. In the south, there's a price to pay for the consistent sunshine of the winter months: the Harmattan. This strong, dusty desert wind can make life difficult. Light clothing is advisable all year round with warmer clothes for winter nights.

| | Climate | **Tropical Wet & Dry** |
| | **Hot Desert** | **Steppe** |

Bamako
Alt: 335m (1,100ft)

	J	F	M	A	M	J	J	A	S	O	N	D
Rainfall												
Comfort												
Sun hrs	9	9	9	8	8	8	7	5	7	8	8	8

Malta

Capital City: **Valletta** World Map ref: **F3**

A good destination for all year sunshine, Malta and its "little sister" island, Gozo, bask in up to 12 hours of sunshine a day in the peak summer and 5 to 6 hours in the winter. The hottest months are July to September but cool sea breezes wafting onto the islands prevent the heat from becoming overpowering. Occasionally in Spring, a very hot and dry wind, the Sirocco, blows in from Africa to bring unpleasantly high temperatures. Rainfall is light in Malta and Gozo and, what little rain there is, falls mainly between October and March.  Light clothing is fine for the long, hot summer although it is always a good idea to take something warmer for the evenings. Take warm cover-ups if visiting in the winter.

Climate   **Mediterranean**

Valletta
Alt: 70m (230ft)

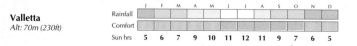

	J	F	M	A	M	J	J	A	S	O	N	D
Rainfall												
Comfort												
Sun hrs	5	6	7	9	10	11	12	11	9	7	6	5

Martinique

Capital City: **Fort-de-France** World Map ref: **C4**

Martinique, one of the Windward Islands, is large, hilly and very French. Rain occurs in all months of the year but is most intense from July to October when there is also the possibility of hurricanes. Downpours are heaviest up in the mountains where temperatures are cooler. The West coast (where Fort-de-France is located) is more sheltered from the prevailing winds. Typically for the Caribbean, the island is consistently hot throughout the year, averaging 8 hours of daily sunshine. Sea breezes help dissipate humidity and prevent the heat getting too sticky.  Take light clothing with warmer cover-ups for trips to higher ground, and go prepared for rain at any time of year.

Fort-de-France
Alt: 5m (16ft)

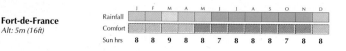

	J	F	M	A	M	J	J	A	S	O	N	D
Rainfall												
Comfort												
Sun hrs	8	8	9	8	8	7	8	8	8	7	8	8

Climate   **Tropical Oceanic**

Mauritania

Capital City: **Nouakchott** World Map ref: **E4**

Another country partly occupied by the vast Sahara Desert, Mauritania has an Atlantic coast which brings sporadic rain to the south between July and October when conditions can be cloudy. Overall, however, the country is hot and dry with the Harmattan winds reducing the effects of humidity over the winter months.  Very light clothing is advisable with warm cover-ups for chillier desert evenings.

Nouakchott
Alt: 2m (7ft)

	J	F	M	A	M	J	J	A	S	O	N	D
Rainfall												
Comfort												
Sun hrs	8	9	10	10	10	10	9	9	9	9	9	8

Climate   **Hot Desert**

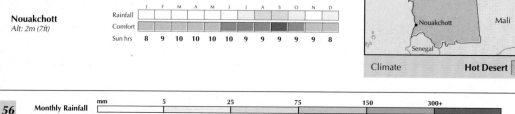

mm	5	25	75	150	300+
in	0.2	1	3	6	12+

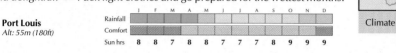

Mauritius

Capital City: **Port Louis**   World Map ref: **G6** (In southern hemisphere)

This pretty volcanic island is a popular holiday retreat largely because of its climate which, although tropical, is tempered by the surrounding seas so that temperatures never soar uncomfortably high. However, high humidity can sometimes make the nights oppressive. Rainfall is substantial throughout the year, particularly on high ground and on the southern coasts which are most exposed to the southeast trade winds. The wettest period is from December to April and, if you are unlucky, you could be caught in an occasional cyclone. From May to November, rainfall is lowest and the weather is generally sunny and delightful. ◖▪ Pack light clothes and go prepared for the wettest months.

Port Louis *Alt: 55m (180ft)*		J	F	M	A	M	J	J	A	S	O	N	D
	Rainfall												
	Comfort												
	Sun hrs	8	8	7	8	8	7	7	7	8	9	9	9

Climate   **Tropical Oceanic**

Mexico

Capital City: **Mexico City**   World Map ref: **B3**

Mexico is a huge country, the largest in Central America, and its sheer size and topography give it a varied climate. Two-thirds of the country consists of plateau and high mountains while its southern half lies within the tropics. Other factors also influence Mexico's weather: the cold California current, which runs southward along its Pacific coast, lowers west coast temperatures and reduces rainfall, giving northwestern regions a desert or semi-desert climate. Northern Mexico's proximity to the great land mass of the United States and Canada brings the region very warm, dry summers and extremely cold winters with snowy spells. The west coast is protected from these climatic extremes by the mountains of Central Mexico while, on the east coast, the warm Caribbean Sea combines with northeast trade winds to create a tropical climate similar to that of the Caribbean islands, with a wet summer season. Indeed, the whole of Mexico receives most of its rain in the summer months (May to October) but the Caribbean coast has the heaviest downpours. The north coast of the Yucatan peninsula witnesses much less rain while the Pacific Coast gets wetter the further south you go. Most of Mexico has a pleasant climate and sunny weather for a large part of the year but the Pacific coast, in the south (where Acapulco is located), and the coasts of the Yucatan, which include Cancun, are affected by heat and high humidity in the summer rainy season. In late summer, both Pacific and Caribbean Coasts can be hit by tropical storms which bring two or three days of heavy rain. In mountainous parts of central Mexico, including Mexico City, temperatures are reduced by the altitude. The northern and central areas of the plateau are dry and arid. ◖▪ Pack light summer clothing supplemented with light jackets or wraps for chillier evenings. Take much warmer clothes if you are going into the highlands or to the north of the country in the winter.

Climate   **Tropical Wet & Dry**
Hot Desert   **Steppe**
Subtropical
High Mountain & Plateau

Acapulco *Alt: 13m (45ft)*		J	F	M	A	M	J	J	A	S	O	N	D
	Rainfall												
	Comfort												
	Sun hrs	9	9	9	8	7	7	7	7	6	7	9	9

Cancun *Alt: 10m (35ft)*		J	F	M	A	M	J	J	A	S	O	N	D
	Rainfall												
	Comfort												
	Sun hrs	5	5	6	6	7	6	6	6	5	5	5	5

Mexico City *Alt: 2,310m (7,600ft)*		J	F	M	A	M	J	J	A	S	O	N	D
	Rainfall												
	Comfort												
	Sun hrs	7	8	8	8	7	7	6	6	6	6	7	7

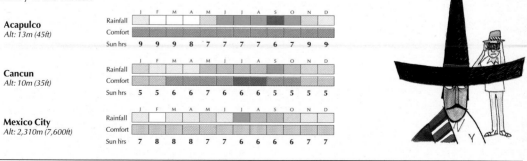

	Cold but tolerable		Hot but tolerable		Danger of Heatstroke	
Extremely Cold		Comfortable, Temperate		Hot & Sticky, Very Hot		

Key to Comfort

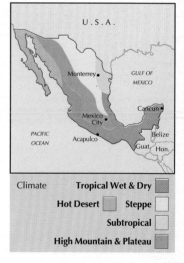

Minorca *see under* Spain

Moldova

Capital City: Kishinev World Map ref: **F2**

Moldova, which is a small landlocked country to the south of the Ukraine, enjoys warm, bright summers with up to 9 hours of sunshine a day. The sun lingers well into the autumn making the weather pleasant, if crisp. However, winters ·can be very cold with occasional heavy snowfalls and icy spells when biting winds come roaring in from Siberia. ◖▶ Pack light clothes for the summer, warmer clothes for the autumn and heavy gear for the chilly winter.

Kishinev *Alt: 95m (310ft)*		J	F	M	A	M	J	J	A	S	O	N	D
	Rainfall												
	Comfort												
	Sun hrs	2	2	4	7	9	9	9	9	7	6	2	1

Climate **Continental**

Monaco

Capital City: Monte Carlo World Map ref: **E2**

This tiny haunt of the beautiful people has the Mediterranean climate essential for maintenance of their golden tans. July and August are the best months for sunworshippers while January and February are the coolest months. Winter conditions are mild but rainy. ◖▶ Take classy beachwear and light clothes for the summer, supplemented by jackets or shawls for chilly evenings. Slightly warmer clothing and a raincoat are appropriate for the winter months.

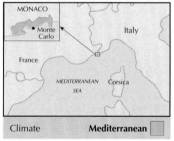

Monte Carlo *Alt: 55m (180ft)*		J	F	M	A	M	J	J	A	S	O	N	D
	Rainfall												
	Comfort												
	Sun hrs	5	5	5	6	7	8	9	9	7	6	5	4

Climate **Mediterranean**

Mongolia

Capital City: Ulan Bator World Map ref: **H2**

Most of Mongolia is a high plateau region with the Gobi desert in the south and grasslands to the north and east. It has a short, warm summer and a very cold winter which lasts for up to seven months and can be extremely harsh. Icy winds make life unpleasant even though snowfall is rare, apart from in the western mountains. ◖▶ Although there are periods of winter sunshine, very heavy clothing is recommended. Even in the summer, you'll need warm clothing.

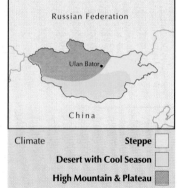

Ulan Bator *Alt: 1,325m (4,300ft)*		J	F	M	A	M	J	J	A	S	O	N	D
	Rainfall												
	Comfort												
	Sun hrs	3	4	5	6	8	7	7	7	6	5	3	2

Climate **Steppe**

Desert with Cool Season

High Mountain & Plateau

mm	5	25	75	150	300+
in	0.2	1	3	6	12+

Montserrat

Capital City: **Plymouth**   World Map ref: **C4**

This lush, volcanic Leeward island was named by Christopher Columbus after the Montserrat Mountain in northern Spain. Rainfall occurs at any time of year but is heaviest from July to November when tropical storms and hurricanes can hit, as Hugo did to such dramatic effect in 1989. A more usual pattern is for rain to fall in short, intense showers sandwiched between periods of bright sunshine. Montserrat is hot and sunny at any time of year and humidity is dispelled by strong sea breezes which make conditions delightful. 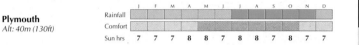 Take light clothing with warmer cover-ups for the occasional chilly winter evening, and be prepared for rain at any time of the year.

	J	F	M	A	M	J	J	A	S	O	N	D
Plymouth Alt: 40m (130ft)	Rainfall												
	Comfort												
	Sun hrs	7	7	7	8	8	7	8	8	7	8	7	7

Climate **Tropical Oceanic**

Morocco

Capital City: **Rabat**   World Map ref: **E3**

Morocco's coastline borders both the Atlantic and the Mediterranean and it has the high Atlas mountainous region inland from the coast which means that its climate is more rainy and temperate than those of other North African countries despite its proximity to the Sahara desert in the south. The weather gets hotter and drier the further south you go and visitors to the southern desert regions should prepare for cold nights, particularly in December and January. On the coast, the winter months, from November to March, tend to be rainy while mountain temperatures are cool. 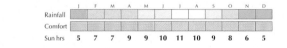 Recommendations on clothing vary depending on the time of year and location. Light clothes are fine during the summer months while warmer clothing is more appropriate during the winter or when up in the mountains. Go prepared if visiting the coast or mountains during the rainy season.

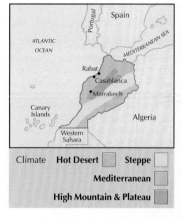

	J	F	M	A	M	J	J	A	S	O	N	D
Rabat Alt: 65m (210ft)	Rainfall												
	Comfort												
	Sun hrs	5	7	7	9	9	10	11	10	9	8	6	5

Climate   **Hot Desert**   **Steppe**

Mediterranean

High Mountain & Plateau

Mozambique

Capital City: **Maputo**   World Map ref: **F5**   (In southern hemisphere)

This is a large country with a 1,200 mile coastline and a tropical climate. There is a single rainy season from November to March but, on the north coast, this lengthens by a few weeks and can bring cyclones. The highlands and south coast bear the brunt of the rains. Temperatures along the coastal lowlands vary: conditions can be warm and pleasant (thanks to sea breezes) or insufferably hot and sweaty during the rainy season when humidity is intense. On higher ground, days are hot but nights cooler with lower humidity. Take light clothing with some warm cover-ups for the highland evenings together with waterproofs if travelling in the rainy season.

	J	F	M	A	M	J	J	A	S	O	N	D
Maputo Alt: 40m (130ft)	Rainfall												
	Comfort												
	Sun hrs	8	8	8	8	8	8	8	8	8	7	7	7

Climate **Tropical Wet & Dry**

Cold but tolerable	Hot but tolerable	Danger of Heatstroke	**Key to Comfort**	**59**
Extremely Cold	Comfortable, Temperate	Hot & Sticky, Very Hot		

Myanmar

Capital City: Yangon   World Map ref: **H3**

Myanmar (formerly Burma) is a large, long, sprawling country with mountains on the coast, to the north and to the east. These take the brunt of the southwest monsoon rains. The central lowlands (including Mandalay) are the driest region. Temperatures reach a peak between March and May, just prior to the arrival of the monsoon and, at this time of the year, humidity is high even inland while coastal areas can feel very clammy indeed. The rains last from May to October and the best time to visit is during the winter (the dry season) when temperatures are lower and conditions bright and fresh with up to 10 hours of sunshine a day. ◼▶ Winter evenings can be cool so it is a good idea to supplement light clothing, needed during the summer months, with warmer attire. The rainy season is hot, so take a light raincoat.

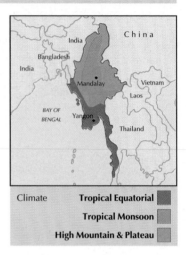

Yangon
Alt: 14m (45ft)

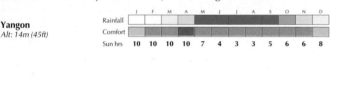

	J	F	M	A	M	J	J	A	S	O	N	D
Rainfall												
Comfort												
Sun hrs	10	10	10	10	7	4	3	3	5	6	6	8

Climate   **Tropical Equatorial**

Tropical Monsoon

High Mountain & Plateau

Namibia

Capital City: Windhoek   World Map ref: **F6**   (In southern hemisphere)

This land contains a big chunk of the Kalahari desert which gives its interior a hot, sunny climate. On the coast, however, it's a different story. Cold sea currents keep temperatures cool and generate plenty of low cloud and fog but almost no rain at any time of year. Inland, rain is sparse, falling between November and April when temperatures are highest. Much of the country's interior is high plateau and this makes night temperatures cool. May to September are the winter months in Namibia when conditions can become cold. ◼▶ Take warm clothing if you are travelling between May and September. Even in the hot months, warm attire is recommended for protection against chilly evenings.

Windhoek
Alt: 1,730m (5,700ft)

	J	F	M	A	M	J	J	A	S	O	N	D
Rainfall												
Comfort												
Sun hrs	9	9	8	9	10	10	10	11	10	10	10	10

Climate   **Hot Desert**   **Steppe**

Nepal

Capital City: Kathmandu   World Map ref: **H3**

This tiny country, which nestles in the Himalayas, has Everest, the world's highest mountain, within its borders. It also has a region of lowland so weather conditions vary according to which part of Nepal you visit. In the high mountains, there is snow and ice throughout the year but a tropical climate prevails in the foothills. The monsoon rains arrive in June and last until September bringing with them a period of muggy, cloudy weather. From October to April, the weather is sunny and warm although lowland nights are cold and temperatures can fall to freezing in the depths of winter. ◼▶ Take light clothing and rainwear in the summer months, light to warm attire for spring and autumn in the foothills and heavier clothes if you are going up into the mountains or visiting in mid-winter.

Kathmandu
Alt: 1,335m (4,400ft)

	J	F	M	A	M	J	J	A	S	O	N	D
Rainfall												
Comfort												
Sun hrs	6	6	8	6	5	2	2	3	5	10	10	9

Climate   **Subtropical**

High Mountain & Plateau

Monthly Rainfall

mm		5		25		75		150		300+
in		0.2		1		3		6		12+

The Netherlands

Capital City: **Amsterdam** World Map ref: **E2**

Large areas of low-lying Holland have been reclaimed from the sea and the country's climate is as changeable as the North Sea waters which lie off its long coast. Be prepared for rain at any time, especially in inland areas which, in the winter, tend to be wetter than coastal districts. In the summer, however, the coast can fall prey to sudden squalls, thunderstorms and intense showers while, in the autumn and winter, it can be afflicted by strong gales. Some winters are severe enough to freeze canals and rivers while others are mild. There are only two things you can be sure of when visiting Holland: the country is very flat and, therefore, windy, and rain can bucket down at any time of year. 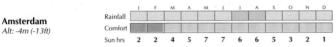 In the summer, you could find yourself basking in up to 8 hours of sunshine a day, so light clothes are appropriate but these should always be supplemented with warmer cover-ups. In winter, medium to warm clothes are essential. Basically, when travelling to Holland, you should be prepared for anything.

Amsterdam
Alt: -4m (-13ft)

	J	F	M	A	M	J	J	A	S	O	N	D
Rainfall												
Comfort												
Sun hrs	2	2	4	5	7	7	6	6	5	3	2	1

Climate   **Maritime**

The Netherlands Antilles

Capital City: **Willemstad** World Map ref: **C4**

The three main islands in this group, Aruba, Curaçao and Bonaire, lie off the coast of Venezuela and share a dry, sunny climate tempered by cool trade winds. There is some rain, mainly from October to January, but this comes in the shape of short, sharp showers. Temperatures are consistently high throughout the year but humidity is low outside the rainy season and this, combined with low rainfall, makes these islands popular holiday retreats. The other islands in the group, St Eustatius, Saba and St Maarten, are located in the Leewards and have a similar climate to Anguilla. 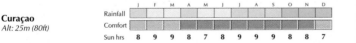 Pack light cotton clothing for any time of year.

Curaçao
Alt: 25m (80ft)

	J	F	M	A	M	J	J	A	S	O	N	D
Rainfall												
Comfort												
Sun hrs	8	9	9	8	7	8	9	9	9	8	8	7

Climate   **Tropical Oceanic**

New Caledonia

Capital City: **Nouméa** World Map ref: **J6** (In southern hemisphere)

A mountainous island in the South Pacific, New Caledonia has a warm but comparatively dry climate, the majority of rain falling in the mountains and on the southern coast which is exposed to the southeast trade winds. December to April are the wettest months and also the hottest and most humid but brisk sea breezes generally prevent conditions from getting too sticky. 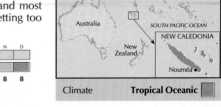 Pack light clothing and a warm wrap for chilly evenings.

Nouméa
Alt: 9m (30ft)

	J	F	M	A	M	J	J	A	S	O	N	D
Rainfall												
Comfort												
Sun hrs	8	8	7	7	6	6	6	7	7	9	8	8

Climate   **Tropical Oceanic**

Cold but tolerable		Hot but tolerable		Danger of Heatstroke	
Extremely Cold		Comfortable, Temperate		Hot & Sticky, Very Hot	

Key to Comfort

New Zealand

Capital City: **Wellington** World Map ref: **J7** (In southern hemisphere)

Given its South Pacific location (1,200 miles (1,900km) from the nearest landmass), New Zealand has a sunnier climate than one might expect. Its North and South Islands are hilly and mountainous with excellent winter sports in the Southern Alps and spectacular fjords and glaciers.

Auckland lies at the top of North Island, the warmest part of New Zealand, and its inhabitants bask in subtropical conditions and enjoy mild winters and warm, humid summers although they can be rained on at any time of the year. On the southern coast, where Wellington and Napier are located, temperatures are slightly lower than in the north and inland conditions can become very frosty during the winter.

South Island, which houses Christchurch and Dunedin, is rather colder than North Island and has more of a maritime climate with little variation in coastal temperatures between summer (October to March) and winter (April to September). Inland, winters are colder with occasional snow on lower ground and heavy snowfalls in the mountains. Rainfall is high on the west coast throughout the year but the Canterbury Plains are the driest part of New Zealand. ◐ Take light clothing if you are travelling in the summer or confining your visit to North Island. On South Island, fairly warm clothes are needed for the winter with heavier wear for trips to the mountains. Whenever you go and wherever you are going, anticipate some rain!

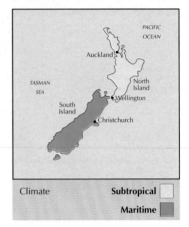

Climate | **Subtropical** ☐
| **Maritime** ▨

Auckland
Alt: 25m (80ft)

	J	F	M	A	M	J	J	A	S	O	N	D
Rainfall												
Comfort												
Sun hrs	7	7	6	5	4	4	4	5	5	6	7	7

Christchurch
Alt: 10m (35ft)

	J	F	M	A	M	J	J	A	S	O	N	D
Rainfall												
Comfort												
Sun hrs	7	7	5	5	4	4	4	5	5	6	7	7

Wellington
Alt: 125m (410ft)

	J	F	M	A	M	J	J	A	S	O	N	D
Rainfall												
Comfort												
Sun hrs	8	7	6	5	4	4	3	4	5	6	7	7

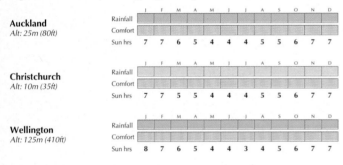

Nicaragua

Capital City: **Managua** World Map ref: **C4**

The largest country in Central America, Nicaragua has a Pacific and a Caribbean coastline and, although hilly, it is less mountainous than other countries in the region. Most of the interior consists of hot tropical lowland or hill country where temperatures are cooler, especially at night. Both coasts are hot, humid and rainy especially during the May to November wet season. Sunshine levels are highest in the winter months (December to April) which bring little rainfall and so make this a good time to visit, especially if you can stay in the hills where the air is crisper. ◐ Take light clothes, warmer cover-ups for the highlands and rainwear in the wet months.

Climate | **Tropical Equatorial** ▨
| **Tropical Wet & Dry** ▨

Managua
Alt: 55m (180ft)

	J	F	M	A	M	J	J	A	S	O	N	D
Rainfall												
Comfort												
Sun hrs	7	8	8	7	6	4	5	6	6	6	7	6

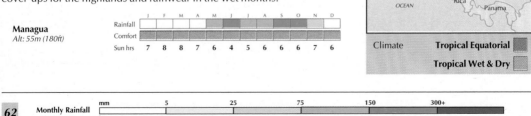

Monthly Rainfall	mm		5		25		75		150		300+	
	in		0.2		1		3		6		12+	

Niger

Capital City: **Niamey** World Map ref: **F4**

Niger is large but sparsely populated and a look at its rainfall chart shows why. The dry months, October to May, are very hot and, although there can be heavy rains in the south during July and August, they are never guaranteed. The north of the country sees scarcely any rain.

For most of the year, light clothing is best, supplemented by warm wraps for cooler evenings.

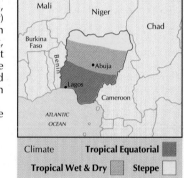

Niamey *Alt: 220m (720ft)*		J	F	M	A	M	J	J	A	S	O	N	D
	Rainfall												
	Comfort												
	Sun hrs	9	9	9	8	9	9	8	7	8	9	10	9

Climate   **Tropical Wet & Dry**

Hot Desert   **Steppe**

Nigeria

Capital City: **Abuja** World Map ref: **F4**

To add to your other problems when visiting Nigeria's main port of Lagos, you are likely to get wet. During the rainy season (from March to November) the coast is the wettest part of the country with an annual fall of more than 2,500mm (100in). Even if it is not raining, you'll end up soaked by the hot, very humid atmosphere. Nigeria's south coast is an unpleasant place to be at any time of year. Inland and further north, matters improve somewhat. The north of the country has the lowest rainfall and the longest, hottest and sunniest dry season (October to April) cooled by the Harmattan winds but, in March to May, temperatures soar before the onset of the rains.

Supplement light clothing with warm wraps for chilly winter nights in the north and you must have good waterproofs for visits to the south.

Lagos *Alt: 5m (16ft)*		J	F	M	A	M	J	J	A	S	O	N	D
	Rainfall												
	Comfort												
	Sun hrs	6	7	6	6	6	5	3	2	3	5	7	7

Climate   **Tropical Equatorial**

Tropical Wet & Dry   **Steppe**

North Korea *see under* Korea, North

Norway

Capital City: **Oslo** World Map ref: **F1**

If you want to make like Scott of the Antarctic, northern Norway is the place to do it. Its Spitzbergen archipelago has an Arctic climate with freezing winters and short summers. There are permanent glaciers and snow fields in the interior and, although summer brings the midnight sun, winter days inflict permanent twilight. Further south, inland winters are still cold and snowy, if not as extreme. Those who prefer more comfortable weather should stay on the coast, which is warmed by the Gulf Stream and remains fairly mild in winter. The coast is, however, very wet and prone to gales.

Take very warm clothing if travelling north in the winter. In the summer months (June to September) much lighter clothing is fine in the southern lowlands but you should supplement this with warmer wraps for visiting the coast, to counter sea breezes. Always have a raincoat at hand.

Oslo *Alt: 95m (310ft)*		J	F	M	A	M	J	J	A	S	O	N	D
	Rainfall												
	Comfort												
	Sun hrs	1	3	5	6	8	8	7	6	5	3	1	1

Climate   **Maritime**   **Icecap**

Subarctic

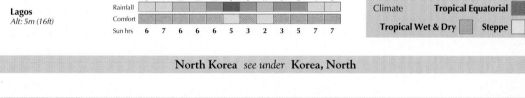

Cold but tolerable	Hot but tolerable	Danger of Heatstroke	**Key to Comfort**
Extremely Cold	Comfortable, Temperate	Hot & Sticky, Very Hot	

Oman

Capital City: **Muscat** World Map ref: **G3**

Avoid Oman in the summer if you can because it grows unpleasantly hot and its south coast, which borders the Arabian Sea, can be cloudy and rainy. Away from the coast, sunshine levels are high throughout the year and there is little rain except in the Jebel Akhdar mountain range in the north and the Dhofar hills in the south. Coastal areas are warm and muggy all year and, although temperatures are higher inland, the air is drier and less oppressive. In the hottest weather, you should take precautions against heatstroke.
 Light clothing is fine all year but should be supplemented by a warm cover-up for chillier winter evenings.

Muscat
Alt: 5m (16ft)

	J	F	M	A	M	J	J	A	S	O	N	D
Rainfall												
Comfort												
Sun hrs	9	10	9	11	12	12	9	10	11	10	10	9

Climate   **Hot Desert**

Pakistan

Capital City: **Islamabad** World Map ref: **G3**

This large country has mountains on two borders, a vast area of low-lying plain and a climate which varies from region to region. The monsoon rains bring cloudy, muggy weather from late June to October and are followed by a period of bright, sunny days and cold to freezing nights until late February. Then temperatures soar and conditions grow unpleasantly hot and dusty until the next arrival of the rains. From March to June, fierce thunderstorms can occur, often exacerbated by accompanying dust storms. The rains are much less intense in the desert region which lies to the south while the Arabian Sea coast experiences little summer rainfall but endures high humidity. The mountains in the north and west receive most of their rain during the cool winter season and are relatively dry during the monsoon although the higher reaches are snowy throughout the year. 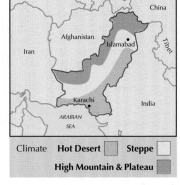 Light clothing with headcovers for the desert region is essential. Take warmer clothing for protection against the cold winter nights and much heavier attire if you are travelling into the mountains.

Climate **Hot Desert**   **Steppe**

High Mountain & Plateau

Karachi
Alt: 4m (13ft)

	J	F	M	A	M	J	J	A	S	O	N	D
Rainfall												
Comfort												
Sun hrs	9	9	9	10	10	8	4	5	7	9	9	9

Panama

Capital City: **Panama City** World Map ref: **C4**

This hilly country is hot throughout the year and the only relief from the high temperatures and humidity is to be found up in the highlands where conditions are cooler and crisper, especially at night. Rainfall is very heavy on the Pacific shoreline and less so (but still substantial) in the lowlands of the Caribbean coast. The rainy season runs from May to December and downpours can be torrential, so always pack good waterproofs if going at this time of year. Sunshine levels are highest in the winter months (January to April) so this is a good time to visit, especially if you can stay in the hills where the air is fresher.  Take light clothes and warmer cover-ups for mountain visits.

Panama City
Alt: 45m (150ft)

	J	F	M	A	M	J	J	A	S	O	N	D
Rainfall												
Comfort												
Sun hrs	8	8	9	8	6	5	5	5	6	5	5	7

Climate   **Tropical Wet & Dry**

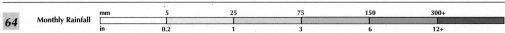
Monthly Rainfall

mm		5	25	75	150	300+
in		0.2	1	3	6	12+

Papua New Guinea

Capital City: **Port Moresby**   World Map ref: **J5**   (In southern hemisphere)

Papua New Guinea, the eastern part of the island of New Guinea, has mountains at its heart and a tropical climate throughout. The south swamplands (which include Port Moresby) have the lowest rainfall but are always humid and oppressive. Higher regions are cooler with snow on the highest peaks and heavy rainfall all year. The north, which includes the Sepik River, endures torrential rains during the northwest monsoon (November to March). 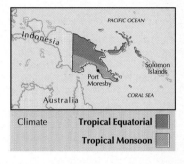 Take light clothing and add heavier clothes and rainwear if you are going to the highlands.

Port Moresby
Alt: 40m (130ft)

	J	F	M	A	M	J	J	A	S	O	N	D
Rainfall												
Comfort												
Sun hrs	6	5	6	7	7	7	7	7	7	7	8	7

Climate   **Tropical Equatorial**
Tropical Monsoon

Paraguay

Capital City: **Asunción**   World Map ref: **C6**   (In southern hemisphere)

The northwest of this landlocked country, the Chaco region, lies within the tropics and has very hot, wet and humid summers (October to March) and warm but drier winters. A rare exception to this rule occurs when Polar air moves outwards from Antarctica and produces cold snaps which send temperatures plummeting for a short while. In the southeast, summers are not quite as hot but are more rainy than in the north and winters are cooler because the terrain is higher. Rain increases the further east you go.
 In the summer (October to March), light clothes should be fine but take warmer clothes for the winter, especially when heading for the southeast. Go prepared for rain whatever the time of year.

Asunción
Alt: 140m (460ft)

	J	F	M	A	M	J	J	A	S	O	N	D
Rainfall												
Comfort												
Sun hrs	9	9	8	8	7	6	6	7	7	8	9	10

Climate   **Tropical Wet & Dry**
Subtropical

Peru

Capital City: **Lima**   World Map ref: **C5**   (In southern hemisphere)

Peru is a large country, twice the size of France, with a long, narrow Pacific coastal plain, the high Andes mountains - which include a substantial area of high plateau - in its interior and a region of low-lying rainforest in the Amazon Basin. The coastal plain, which has Lima at its centre, has a desert-like climate with minimal rainfall throughout the year. The cold ocean current produces a lot of cloud and mist which obscures the sun and prevents the permanently high temperatures from becoming excessive. In the mountains, it's a different story: temperatures drop lower the higher up you go. The slopes of the Andes are semi-tropical but, on higher ground, night time temperatures can be extremely cold and frosts are frequent during the dry season. The high peaks are permanently snowcapped. On the Andean plateau, rainfall is low and occurs mainly from December to March. The two main hazards you'll encounter here are altitude sickness and sunburn: the air is very thin at 3,000m (10,000 ft), so you should be prepared to acclimatise slowly. The lowlands have a hot, steamy equatorial climate with a single heavy rainy season from November to February when temperatures are highest.  Pack light cotton clothing plus rainwear for the Amazon Basin, warmer clothes for the evenings and winters on the coast and much warmer clothing for the mountains.

Lima
Alt: 120m (390ft)

	J	F	M	A	M	J	J	A	S	O	N	D
Rainfall												
Comfort												
Sun hrs	6	7	7	7	4	1	1	1	1	3	4	5

Climate   **Tropical Equatorial**
Tropical Wet & Dry
Hot Desert
High Mountain & Plateau

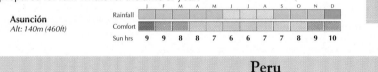

Extremely Cold	Cold but tolerable	Comfortable, Temperate	Hot but tolerable	Hot & Sticky, Very Hot	Danger of Heatstroke

Key to Comfort

Philippines

Capital City: **Manila**   World Map ref: **I4**

This archipelago of more than 7,000 islands has a hot, steamy, equatorial climate in the south with heavy rainfall all year. In the north and central Philippines, a tropical climate prevails with a single rainy season which can run from late May to early November. The heaviest rains occur from July to October. Swept in by ferocious typhoons from the South China Sea, these can sometimes cause extensive damage and loss of life. The summers are hot, cloudy and often muggy and oppressive. Many of the Philippine islands are mountainous and, although a trip to the highlands may bring relief from the high temperatures lower down, the higher reaches frequently experience heavy cloud and rainfall. The best time to visit is during the dry winter months (November to February) when conditions are sunny and pleasant and sea breezes dissipate humidity. ▣ Light clothing is appropriate for any time of the year but should be supplemented with slightly warmer attire for mountain visits and chilly evenings. Be well prepared for the heavy rains in the summer months.

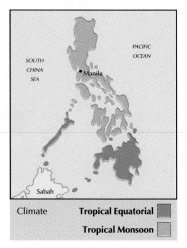

Manila
Alt: 13m (45ft)

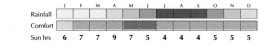

	J	F	M	A	M	J	J	A	S	O	N	D
Rainfall												
Comfort												
Sun hrs	6	7	7	9	7	5	4	4	4	5	5	5

Climate   **Tropical Equatorial** ▣
            Tropical Monsoon ▣

Poland

Capital City: **Warsaw**   World Map ref: **F2**

The major part of Poland consists of a flat, rolling plain but the country also has a Baltic coastline and mountain ranges to the south, so its weather varies according to the region. Winters are colder in the southeast which holds the Carpathian mountain range. Temperatures here fall as altitude increases. The whole country sees snow in winter and this can lie for up to three months in the mountains. The mildest winters and coolest summers are to be found on the Baltic Coast. Summer temperatures throughout Poland are warm rather than hot, with a maximum of 8 hours daily sunshine. ▣ Weather can be changeable, so supplement light summer clothes with warmer cover-ups and a raincoat. Much warmer clothes are needed for the winter which can be really cold.

Warsaw
Alt: 110m (360ft)

	J	F	M	A	M	J	J	A	S	O	N	D
Rainfall												
Comfort												
Sun hrs	2	2	3	5	8	8	7	7	5	4	2	1

Climate   **Continental** ▣

Portugal

Capital City: **Lisbon**   World Map ref: **E3**

Portugal's southerly position makes it Europe's answer to California in terms of climate, although its hot summers can be tempered by weather fronts moving in from the Atlantic. The best place for summer sunseekers is the south coast where the sea is the warmest and the summers are long, dry and very hot but tempered by sea breezes: hence the popularity of the Algarve. The mildest, driest winters are also to be found in the south although everywhere in Portugal can be rainy in the winter months. The heaviest downpours take place in the north and can begin there in early autumn. The

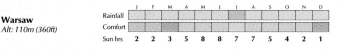

mm		5	25	75	150	300+
in		0.2	1	3	6	12+

Portugal - *continued*

north of Portugal is higher in altitude than the south and can, therefore, witness snow in the winter, although this is sporadic and of short duration. ▥ Pack light clothes for the summer months and supplement these with warmer attire for the autumn and winter. Take a raincoat in the winter months.

Climate   **Mediterranean** ▢

            Maritime ▣

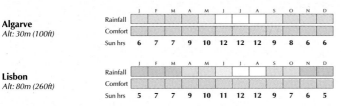

Algarve
Alt: 30m (100ft)

	J	F	M	A	M	J	J	A	S	O	N	D
Rainfall												
Comfort												
Sun hrs	6	7	7	9	10	12	12	12	9	8	6	6

Lisbon
Alt: 80m (260ft)

	J	F	M	A	M	J	J	A	S	O	N	D
Rainfall												
Comfort												
Sun hrs	5	7	7	9	10	11	12	12	9	7	6	5

The Azores

These mountainous islands are part of Portugal and they make a good retreat for those who hate extremes of temperature: summers are warm and sunny but never uncomfortably hot while winters are mild, but wet. ▥ Take light clothing with warm cover-ups for the summer months and medium to warm clothing for the winter months.

Madeira

The Madeira group of islands are an integral part of Portugal and lie around 450 miles off the coast of Morocco. The main island of Madeira is mountainous and volcanic and has a Mediterranean climate tempered by the seas which surround it. You'll rarely feel uncomfortably hot or unpleasantly cold on Madeira but expect to be rained on in the winter months, especially on higher ground. On this island, you'll find the weather can change dramatically the higher up you go, so you can progress from bright sunshine on the coast to chilly fog and heavy rain within the course of a morning. ▥ You should always supplement light clothing with warm cover-ups in summer and take medium to warm clothes for the winter months. Rain is sparse in mid summer (May to September) but take a raincoat at other times of the year.

Madeira - Funchal
Alt: 60m (200ft)

	J	F	M	A	M	J	J	A	S	O	N	D
Rainfall												
Comfort												
Sun hrs	5	6	6	7	7	7	8	8	8	7	5	5

Weather Statistics for 315 locations around the world *see pages 94-103*

Puerto Rico

Capital City: **San Juan**   World Map ref: **C4**

This large, mountainous island lies between Hispaniola and the Leewards and its topography and location, in the path of the northeast trade winds, gives it a rainier climate than is usual in the region. Unlike most other Caribbean islands, which have a single summer rainy season, Puerto Rico experiences downpours at any time of the year. Its centre and north coast (site of the island's capital, San Juan) are particularly rainy. The south coast is more sheltered and therefore drier. Temperatures are high throughout the year in San Juan and humidity can make the heat sticky and unpleasant, although sea breezes help dispel this on the coast and the air is cooler and fresher in the mountains. ▥ Pack light clothes and rainwear with a warmer cover-up if you are planning a mountain visit.

Climate   **Tropical Equatorial** ▣

San Juan
Alt: 25m (80ft)

	J	F	M	A	M	J	J	A	S	O	N	D
Rainfall												
Comfort												
Sun hrs	7	8	9	9	8	8	8	9	7	8	7	7

Cold but tolerable		Hot but tolerable		Danger of Heatstroke		
Extremely Cold		Comfortable, Temperate		Hot & Sticky, Very Hot	**Key to Comfort**	**67**

Qatar

Capital City: **Doha** World Map ref: **G3**

This small peninsula, which lies on the north coast of Saudi Arabia, is more pleasant to visit in winter than in summer. Winter, spring and autumn days are warm and sunny, with occasional light rainfall, while the summer months are uncomfortably hot and very dry. Although summer temperatures are slightly lower on the coast, high humidity creates an oppressive environment and, in the hottest weather, there is a danger of heatstroke for the unwary. Light clothes are essential in the summer heat but take slightly warmer attire if you are visiting in the winter.

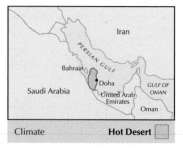

Doha
Alt: 3m (10ft)

	J	F	M	A	M	J	J	A	S	O	N	D
Rainfall												
Comfort												
Sun hrs	8	8	8	9	10	11	11	10	10	10	9	8

Climate   **Hot Desert**

Réunion

Capital City: **St Denis** World Map ref: **G6** (In southern hemisphere)

This volcanic island lies around 120 miles southwest of Mauritius and has similar weather to that of the larger island. Rainfall is substantial throughout the year but particularly between December and April when cyclones can hit. From May to November, conditions are largely sunny and warm with high humidity tempered by sea breezes. Take light clothing with rainwear and warmer cover-ups if planning to climb the volcano.

St Denis
Alt: 10m (35ft)

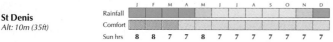

	J	F	M	A	M	J	J	A	S	O	N	D
Rainfall												
Comfort												
Sun hrs	8	8	7	7	8	7	7	7	7	7	7	7

Climate   **Tropical Oceanic**

Rhodes *see under* **Greece**

Romania

Capital City: **Bucharest** World Map ref: **F2**

Romania's climate is similar to that of the Russian plains with severe winters and warm summers. Rainfall is fairly low and concentrated in the winter months when it is often accompanied by storms. Snow falls in the lowlands for about one month in the winter but the Carpathian Mountains can be snow-covered for up to four months. The best place to spend the winter is on the Black Sea coast where milder conditions prevail. Inland, temperatures plunge low enough to freeze the rivers. In the summer, sea level inland areas are the hottest; coastal temperatures are moderated by sea breezes while, up in the mountains, the summers are cool and rainy. The weather can be quirky at any time of the year. Winds, roaring in from the Russian Steppes, can bring scorching droughts in the summer and icy blasts in winter. Keep summer clothes mainly light if you are visiting the coast or the lowlands but take warmer wear for the winter and the mountains. Be prepared for rain.

Bucharest
Alt: 90m (300ft)

	J	F	M	A	M	J	J	A	S	O	N	D
Rainfall												
Comfort												
Sun hrs	2	3	5	6	8	9	11	10	8	5	2	2

Climate   **Continental**

Monthly Rainfall

mm		5		25		75		150		300+
in		0.2		1		3		6		12+

Russian Federation

Capital City: **Moscow** World Map ref: **G1-J1**

European Russia

This vast region stretches north to the Arctic Coast, west to the Ural Mountains and South to the Caucasus Mountains. Moscow and St Petersburg are in the central half of European Russia which has warm, wet summers but very severe winters. The Russian winter is legendary: it defeated both Napoleon and Hitler.  Thermal underwear, heavy clothes and fur caps are essential if you are visiting between November and April. In the summer, light clothing should be supplemented with warmer cover-ups and a raincoat.

The northern part of Russia, which includes the ports of Murmansk and Archangel, is a sub-arctic region and extends into the Arctic Circle: not a place for package tourists. If you have to go there between October and April, take thermals and very heavy windproof and waterproof clothing.

The south includes both a steppe region to the west of the Caspian Sea and the "Russian Riviera" on the east coast of the Black Sea. The Steppes have scorchingly hot summers and very cold winters. Black Sea summers are hot and sunny and winters milder although coastal districts are prone to heavy rain at any time of the year. Light clothing is suitable for the summers. Take much heavier clothes for the winter. Always be prepared for rain on the Black Sea coast.

EUROPEAN RUSSIA

Climate

	Steppe
Continental	Icecap
	Subarctic
High Mountain & Plateau	

Moscow
Alt: 155m (510ft)

	J	F	M	A	M	J	J	A	S	O	N	D
Rainfall												
Comfort												
Sun hrs	1	3	4	5	8	9	9	8	6	3	1	0

Russia/Siberia

This immense region covers one tenth of the world's surface. Stretching from the Ural Mountains in the West to the Pacific Ocean in the east, it is famous for the severity of its winters. Its northern territory lies within the Arctic Circle so, here, summers are very short and the long winter is particularly ferocious. Extreme winter conditions prevail throughout the country and spring and autumn are virtually unknown seasons: temperatures rise suddenly and sharply at the onset of the summer months and plunge dramatically as winter starts to grip. The worst winter conditions arise not from heavy snowfall but from biting winds which are sometimes powerful enough to blow snow cover from the ground. To the south, the Russian Steppes attract hotter, drier weather in the summer months, turning bitterly cold with strong winds in the winter. Summer is the wettest season throughout the region.

Don't endure the Russian winter unless you absolutely have to. If you must, take layers of very heavy clothes (invest in a warm hat which covers the ears and a warm scarf for the face!) and take time to acclimatise. In the summer, always mix warmer clothes and a raincoat with lightweights.

ASIAN RUSSIA

Climate

	Steppe
Continental	Icecap
	Subarctic
High Mountain & Plateau	

Vladivostok
Alt: 30m (100ft)

	J	F	M	A	M	J	J	A	S	O	N	D
Rainfall												
Comfort												
Sun hrs	6	7	7	6	6	5	4	5	7	7	6	6

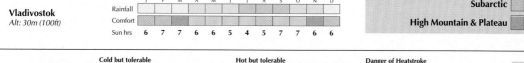

Cold but tolerable	Hot but tolerable	Danger of Heatstroke
Extremely Cold	Comfortable, Temperate	Hot & Sticky, Very Hot

Key to Comfort

Rwanda

Capital City: **Kigali** World Map ref: **F5** (In southern hemisphere)

Rwanda is a mountainous country and its high altitudes keep temperatures moderate in the lower reaches and cool in the hills. The rainy season is from October to May. The best time to visit is between June and August when humidity is relatively low and conditions are pleasant.  Despite its high altitude, temperatures in Rwanda are high enough to justify light clothing unless you're planning a walk in the mountains. Pack some warm clothes for the evenings and be prepared for the rainy season.

Kigali
Alt: 1,490m (4,900ft)

	J	F	M	A	M	J	J	A	S	O	N	D
Rainfall												
Comfort												
Sun hrs	5	4	5	5	5	7	8	7	7	6	5	4

Climate	**Tropical Wet & Dry**

St Kitts & Nevis

Capital City: **Basseterre** World Map ref: **C4**

St Kitts, and her smaller sister Nevis (pronounced Neevis), lie in the Leeward Islands to the west of Antigua. They are hilly and volcanic and experience some rain all year. July to November is the rainy season when there is the possibility of hurricanes. These typical Caribbean islands are delightfully hot and sunny at any time of the year. Temperatures are never excessive and trade winds counter the effects of heat and humidity. 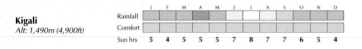 Light cotton clothing is appropriate for any time of the year with cover-ups for the occasional chilly winter evening.

St Kitts
Alt: 30m (100ft)

	J	F	M	A	M	J	J	A	S	O	N	D
Rainfall												
Comfort												
Sun hrs	8	8	9	9	9	9	9	9	9	8	8	8

Climate	**Tropical Oceanic**

St Lucia

Capital City: **Castries** World Map ref: **C4**

St Lucia, one of the Windward Islands, is large and mountainous with volcanic peaks. It attracts more rain than is normal for the Caribbean. This falls mainly from May to January and is most intense during the July to November hurricane season when tropical storms can make life difficult even if they don't hit the island directly. The west coast (where Castries is located) is more sheltered from the prevailing winds. Temperatures on St Lucia are high throughout the year but rarely unbearable since sea breezes help dissipate the humidity, although nights can be sticky. 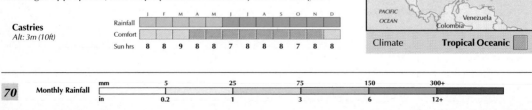 Light cotton clothing is appropriate, and be prepared for rain at any time of the year.

Castries
Alt: 3m (10ft)

	J	F	M	A	M	J	J	A	S	O	N	D
Rainfall												
Comfort												
Sun hrs	8	8	9	8	8	7	8	8	8	7	8	8

Climate	**Tropical Oceanic**

mm		5	25	75	150	300+
in		0.2	1	3	6	12+

St Vincent & The Grenadines

Capital City: Kingstown World Map ref: **C4**

St Vincent is part of an island group which includes the Grenadines (a yachtsman's paradise) and exclusive Mustique. St Vincent itself is large and mountainous. Rainfall is substantial throughout the year and downpours are most intense from July to December with the possibility of hurricanes between July and November. Like the other Caribbean islands, it has a warm, sunny climate all year. Summer is hotter than winter but temperatures are never extreme. Even during its hottest months, the island is a pleasant place to be since sea breezes help dissipate humidity. However, nights can be sticky. Light cotton clothing is appropriate for any time of the year as well as cover-ups for the occasional chilly winter night.

St Vincent
Alt: 9m (30ft)

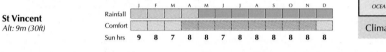

	J	F	M	A	M	J	J	A	S	O	N	D
Rainfall												
Comfort												
Sun hrs	9	8	7	8	8	7	8	8	8	8	8	8

Climate   **Tropical Oceanic**

Sardinia *see under* Italy

Saudi Arabia

Capital City: Riyadh World Map ref: **G3**

You are unlikely to need an umbrella in Saudi Arabia: it is one of the driest countries in the world with vast tracts of desert which attract less than 200mm (8in) of rainfall a year. What rainfall there is comes between November and May, except in the mountains of the southwest where light rainfall is possible at any time of year. The mountains are the best place to be in the height of summer when inland areas can bake in temperatures as high as 48°C (118°F). The heat is exacerbated on the Persian Gulf and Red Sea coasts by high humidity which keep nights hot and sticky: there is some danger of heat exhaustion or even heat stroke in the hottest areas. Inland, lower humidity levels bring a sharp drop in temperatures at night and can cause frosts in winter. Light, loose clothing is ideal for a visit to Saudi at any time of year but you should take warmer clothing to cope with air-conditioning and for chilly nights when venturing into the desert.

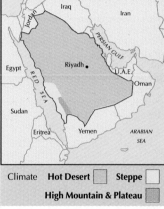

Riyadh
Alt: 590m (1,950ft)

	J	F	M	A	M	J	J	A	S	O	N	D
Rainfall												
Comfort												
Sun hrs	7	8	7	8	9	11	11	10	9	10	9	7

Climate   **Hot Desert**   **Steppe**
High Mountain & Plateau

Senegal

Capital City: Dakar World Map ref: **E4**

The best time to visit Senegal is between December and April during the dry season. At this time, temperatures are cooler and hot desert winds, although dusty, disperse the humidity and make life more comfortable. In the rainy season (June to September), the sticky heat will drive you mad, especially on the coast, when heavy cloud cover frequently obscures the sun and nights are as hot and humid as the days. The further north you go, the less rain you'll see. Northern Senegal borders the Sahara Desert so days are hot and nights chilly. Even on the coast, winter trade winds can be cool. Supplement light clothing with warm cover-ups, just in case.

Dakar
Alt: 30m (100ft)

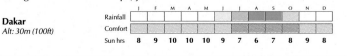

	J	F	M	A	M	J	J	A	S	O	N	D
Rainfall												
Comfort												
Sun hrs	8	9	10	10	10	9	7	6	7	8	9	8

Climate   **Tropical Wet & Dry**
Steppe

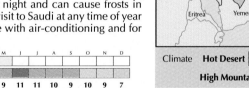

Cold but tolerable	Hot but tolerable	Danger of Heatstroke
Extremely Cold	Comfortable, Temperate	Hot & Sticky, Very Hot

Key to Comfort

Seychelles

Capital City: **Victoria**   World Map ref: **G5**   (In southern hemisphere)

Most of these 90 Indian Ocean islands are low-lying although Mahe, the largest in the group, has a hilly terrain. They lie outside the cyclone belt but rainfall everywhere is moderate to heavy all year particularly between October and March and on their southern coasts which are exposed to the southeast trade winds. Despite all the rain, the climate is delightfully sunny with temperatures high but tolerable and humidity tempered by soft ocean breezes, hence the islands' popularity with holidaymakers. The driest months are June to August. ▥ Take light clothing and anticipate rain at any time of year.

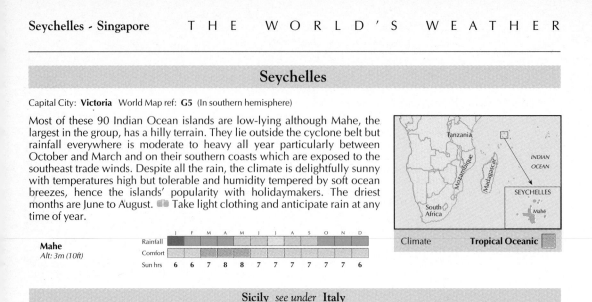

Mahe		J	F	M	A	M	J	J	A	S	O	N	D
Alt: 3m (10ft)	Rainfall												
	Comfort												
	Sun hrs	6	6	7	8	8	7	7	7	7	7	7	6

Climate   **Tropical Oceanic**

Sicily *see under* **Italy**

Sierra Leone

Capital City: **Freetown**   World Map ref: **E4**

Sierra Leone has an Atlantic coastline and an inland plain leading to hill country so the further inland you go, the hotter and drier the weather. Humidity is unpleasantly high on the coast and, during the very heavy rainy season, between May and November, this combines with heavy cloud to make life very uncomfortable. Matters improve during the dry season when sunny, bright weather predominates and the Harmattan desert winds blow. Temperatures are high all year. ▥ Take light clothing but go prepared for very heavy downpours during the rainy season, particularly from July to September.

Freetown		J	F	M	A	M	J	J	A	S	O	N	D
Alt: 11m (35ft)	Rainfall												
	Comfort												
	Sun hrs	8	8	8	7	6	5	3	2	4	6	7	7

Climate   **Tropical Equatorial**

Tropical Monsoon

Singapore

Capital City: **Singapore**   World Map ref: **H4**

Singapore is a tiny state at the southern tip of the Malay Peninsula. It has an equatorial climate with average temperatures in the high 20s Centigrade (low 80s Fahrenheit). High humidity makes conditions steamy and particularly unbearable in March and September when there is hardly any breeze. Rain can bucket down at any time of the year although it is most likely between November and January when the northeasterly monsoon brings short, sharp, intense showers. ▥ Take light clothes and remember that air-conditioning in the airport, taxi and hotel can be chilly, so always have a light jacket or wrap to hand.

Singapore		J	F	M	A	M	J	J	A	S	O	N	D
Alt: 11m (35ft)	Rainfall												
	Comfort												
	Sun hrs	5	7	6	6	6	6	6	6	5	5	5	4

Climate   **Tropical Equatorial**

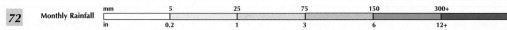

Monthly Rainfall

mm		5	25	75	150	300+
in		0.2	1	3	6	12+

Slovakia

Capital City: **Bratislava** World Map ref: **F2**

The Slovak Republic, which was part of Czechoslovakia until 1993, is a hilly, landlocked state in Central Europe. Its central position brings a mixed climate influenced both by the mild, wet weather of Atlantic Europe and the hot summers and icy winters of Russia. As a result, summers are warm but frequently rainy, prone to disturbances blowing in from the north Mediterranean. Winters are cold and wet, particularly on high ground where heavy snows linger for up to four months. An occasional spell of settled winter weather can bring a run of cold but crisp, bright days but life gets very nasty when easterly winds howl in from Russia bringing severe cold snaps. Wrap up warmly for a winter visit and supplement lighter clothing with warm cover-ups, even in the summer. Go prepared for rain whatever the time of year.

Climate **Continental**

Bratislava
Alt: 155m (510ft)

	J	F	M	A	M	J	J	A	S	O	N	D
Rainfall												
Comfort												
Sun hrs	2	3	5	7	9	9	9	9	7	5	2	1

Slovenia

Capital City: **Ljubljana** World Map ref: **F2**

Mountainous Slovenia has a continental climate which means warm summers and cold winters, especially in the Dinaric Alps which experience heavy snowfalls and a lot of summer rain. On lower ground, summer temperatures are high but sunny days can be interrupted by fierce thunderstorms, while winter can bring the icy blast of the very nasty Bora wind which whistles in from Eastern Europe. Light summer clothing should be supplemented with rainwear. In winter, take much warmer clothing.

Climate **Continental**

Ljubljana
Alt: 300m (980ft)

	J	F	M	A	M	J	J	A	S	O	N	D
Rainfall												
Comfort												
Sun hrs	2	3	4	5	6	7	8	7	5	3	1	1

Solomon Islands

Capital City: **Honiara** World Map ref: **J5** (In southern hemisphere)

The Solomons lie east of New Guinea and comprise many hundreds of islands, the largest being mountainous and forested. Expect hot, sticky weather at any time of year, when visiting these islands, although strong sea breezes help make the clammy conditions more bearable. Rainfall is substantial throughout the year and is heaviest between December and April when there are frequent tropical storms, and downpours can be torrential. Pack lightweight clothing and good waterproofs for any time of the year.

Climate **Tropical Equatorial**

Honiara
Alt: 8m (25ft)

	J	F	M	A	M	J	J	A	S	O	N	D
Rainfall												
Comfort												
Sun hrs	6	5	5	6	7	6	6	4	7	6	6	6

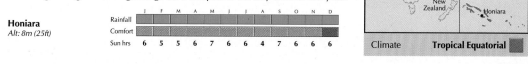

Cold but tolerable   Hot but tolerable   Danger of Heatstroke
Extremely Cold   Comfortable, Temperate   Hot & Sticky, Very Hot   **Key to Comfort**

Somalia

Capital City: Mogadishu World Map ref: **G4**

Somalia lies within the Horn of Africa and, although its coast borders the Indian Ocean and the Gulf of Aden, vast tracts of the country are desert. This gives it a hot, dry climate with unreliable rain. There is very little rain in the North and, elsewhere, what rain there is falls between May and November. Coastal conditions are cooler in the east where the rainy season can bring fog and heavy cloud but, on the north coast, temperatures between April and September can be ferociously hot and this, combined with high humidity, brings a risk of heat exhaustion for the unwary. 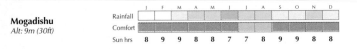 Light clothing is appropriate throughout the year supplemented by slightly warmer attire for the eastern coast during the rainy season.

Mogadishu Alt: 9m (30ft)		J	F	M	A	M	J	J	A	S	O	N	D
	Rainfall												
	Comfort												
	Sun hrs	8	9	9	8	8	7	7	8	9	9	8	8

Climate   **Hot Desert** ▢   **Steppe** ▢

South Africa

Capital City: Pretoria World Map ref: **F6** (In southern hemisphere)

A pleasant climate is a major asset in South Africa's drive to distance itself from past controversy and place itself firmly on the world tourism map. If travelling to South Africa, remember that, because it lies south of the equator, its seasons are the opposite to ours.

Only the low-lying areas in the north, along the borders with Zimbabwe and Mozambique, have a tropical climate with related high temperatures and humidity. In the south, the coastal lowlands around Cape Town have a Mediterranean-type climate with hot summers (during our winter months) and warm, rainy winters.

The eastern coastlands and the low veld of Durban and Natal have a subtropical climate with most rainfall falling between October and April which is also the period of highest temperatures and humidity. The western coastal strip has a cold sea current which keeps temperatures cool and generates plenty of low cloud and fog but almost no rain.

In the eastern interior or high veld (where Johannesburg and Pretoria are situated), summers (our winters) are rainy and warm and winter days are mild although temperatures can drop dramatically at night. The low humidity and high number of sunshine hours produce a pleasant and healthy climate all year. The western interior is mostly desert or semi-desert and has a hot, sunny climate. What rain there is falls between November and April. 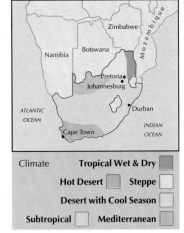 Take light clothing and be prepared for rain if travelling in our winter (South Africa's summer) and warmer wear if travelling in our summer months.

Climate   **Tropical Wet & Dry** ▢

Hot Desert ▢   **Steppe** ▢

Desert with Cool Season ▢

Subtropical ▢   **Mediterranean** ▢

Cape Town Alt: 40m (130ft)		J	F	M	A	M	J	J	A	S	O	N	D
	Rainfall												
	Comfort												
	Sun hrs	11	10	9	8	6	6	6	7	8	9	10	11

Durban Alt: 15m (50ft)		J	F	M	A	M	J	J	A	S	O	N	D
	Rainfall												
	Comfort												
	Sun hrs	6	7	7	7	7	8	7	7	6	6	5	6

Johannesburg Alt: 1,675m (5,500ft)		J	F	M	A	M	J	J	A	S	O	N	D
	Rainfall												
	Comfort												
	Sun hrs	8	8	8	8	9	9	9	10	10	9	8	8

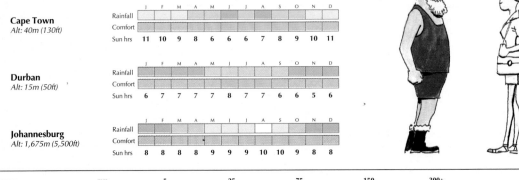

Monthly Rainfall

mm	5	25	75	150	300+
in	0.2	1	3	6	12+

South Korea *see under* **Korea, South**

Spain

Capital City: **Madrid**   World Map ref: **E3**

Spain is endowed with both mountainous and lowland regions and, with the stormy Atlantic lying off one coast the balmy Mediterranean off the other, it is a land of many climates. Those who associate Spain with the sunniness of its Mediterranean region will be in for a shock if they travel to the north where clouds and rain are frequently blown in from the Atlantic to cast a blight over warm summer days. Rainfall eases off as you pass from west to east along the Pyrenees: the mountains and coast of north and northwest Spain are the wettest parts of the country and receive some rain every month.

In central Spain, most precipitation falls in the winter months and takes the form of mountain snow. Summers are hot, long and very dry, plagued by searing dusty winds. What rain there is comes in spring and very early summer, usually in short, intense bursts. Summer lasts longer the further south you go.

The eastern and southern coasts of Spain hold the Mediterranean resorts we all know and love. Here, you'll find oodles of sunshine (up to 12 hours a day in summer) tempered by gentle sea breezes. In the south, however, beware of the Leveche, a hot African wind which sometimes makes the summertime heat unbearable. Most of the area sees very little rain in the summer but, if you venture north of Valencia, you could encounter the occasional fierce thunderstorm. 🧳 Light clothing is fine for summers spent in central Spain or the Mediterranean coast. Take cover-ups for the winter months and much warmer clothing for central Spain. If you are visiting the north, take slightly warmer attire and be prepared for rain.

Climate	
Mediterranean	
Maritime	
High Mountain & Plateau	

Barcelona
Alt: 95m (310ft)

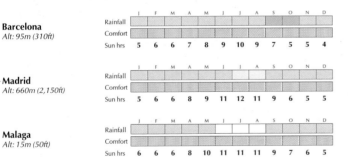

	J	F	M	A	M	J	J	A	S	O	N	D
Rainfall												
Comfort												
Sun hrs	5	6	6	7	8	9	10	9	7	5	5	4

Madrid
Alt: 660m (2,150ft)

	J	F	M	A	M	J	J	A	S	O	N	D
Rainfall												
Comfort												
Sun hrs	5	6	6	8	9	11	12	11	9	6	5	5

Malaga
Alt: 15m (50ft)

	J	F	M	A	M	J	J	A	S	O	N	D
Rainfall												
Comfort												
Sun hrs	6	6	6	8	10	11	11	11	9	7	6	5

The Balearic Islands

The Balearics, of which the best known are Majorca, Minorca and Ibiza, are popular holiday spots throughout the year thanks to their Mediterranean climate which brings hot summers and warm winters. Even at the height of summer, these islands are a delight because on them the sun's rays are tempered by gentle sea breezes and, in the winter, you can look forward to 5 hours of sunshine a day. Rainfall is generally light, particularly during the summer months but rain can fall at any time and winter showers can be heavy. 🧳 Even in the summer, supplement light clothes and beach wear with a warm cover-up for breezy evenings. In winter you'll need warmer clothing - the evenings can be cold.

Majorca - Palma
Alt: 10m (35ft)

	J	F	M	A	M	J	J	A	S	O	N	D
Rainfall												
Comfort												
Sun hrs	5	6	6	7	10	10	11	10	8	6	5	4

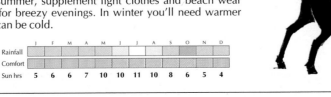

	Cold but tolerable		Hot but tolerable		Danger of Heatstroke	
Extremely Cold		Comfortable, Temperate		Hot & Sticky, Very Hot	

Key to Comfort

Spain - *continued*

The Canary Islands

This seven-island archipelago has a Mediterranean-type climate with almost no rainfall in the summer months. Winters are rainier, especially in the north. The islands are rocky and volcanic and have snow on their highest peaks although, at sea-level, summers are warm and winters very mild with occasional fog. The cold Canaries current of the Atlantic Ocean prevents summer temperatures from climbing uncomfortably high. The warmest days occur when hot, dry, dust-laden air is drawn out of the Sahara desert and reaches as far as the islands. ▦ Light clothing is fine for summer. Take slightly warmer wear in the winter months.

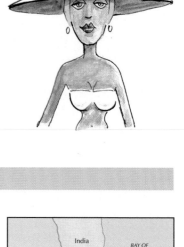

Gran Canaria - Las Palmas		J	F	M	A	M	J	J	A	S	O	N	D
	Rainfall												
Alt: 25m (80ft)	Comfort												
	Sun hrs	6	6	7	8	8	9	9	9	8	7	6	6

Sri Lanka

Capital City: **Colombo** World Map ref: **H4**

Although this island's interior is mountainous, its climate is consistently warm and sunny and conditions rarely grow chilly, even at night. In the lowland areas around the coast, temperatures are much higher and humidity can make evenings rather clammy, although sea breezes keep daytimes fairly fresh. Expect rain on this island at any time of the year: rainfall is most intense in the southwest from April to June and from October to November. Rain tends to fall mainly in the afternoons and can be accompanied by thunderstorms. The driest conditions are found in the northeast which has only one main rainy season (from October to January). ▦ You'll need light clothes for a trip to Sri Lanka.

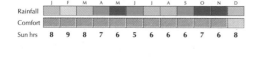

Colombo		J	F	M	A	M	J	J	A	S	O	N	D
	Rainfall												
Alt: 7m (25ft)	Comfort												
	Sun hrs	8	9	8	7	6	5	6	6	6	7	6	8

Climate	Tropical Equatorial
	Tropical Monsoon

Sudan

Capital City: **Khartoum** World Map ref: **F4**

Africa's largest country consists of hot desert to the north with the likelihood of rain increasing the further south you go. The main rainy season is from April to October but, in the far south, rain can fall during any month. In the north, extremely high summer temperatures are made tolerable, to some extent, by low humidity. The south is cooler with higher humidity but beware the Haboob (strong winds producing violent but brief dust or even sand storms). In the winter, night time temperatures in the desert can be low and you may even see an occasional frost at dawn. ▦ Expect to have to wrap up warmly if you are travelling to northern Sudan between November and March. Otherwise, light clothing is fine but go prepared for rain if you are venturing further south.

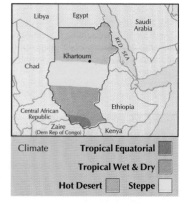

Khartoum		J	F	M	A	M	J	J	A	S	O	N	D
	Rainfall												
Alt: 380m (1,250ft)	Comfort												
	Sun hrs	11	11	10	11	10	10	9	9	10	10	11	11

Climate	Tropical Equatorial
	Tropical Wet & Dry
Hot Desert	Steppe

mm	5	25	75	150	300+
in	0.2	1	3	6	12+

Surinam

Capital City: Paramaribo World Map ref: **D4**

Surinam has a narrow low-lying Atlantic coastal plain but the rest of the country is hilly and forested. It has an Equatorial climate which is warm, wet and humid throughout the year with heavy rains from May to July and again from November to January. The northeast trade winds bring some relief on the coast and you can escape the sticky heat and rain by moving to higher ground inland. Here, temperatures are cooler, especially at night, and rain is lighter, falling mainly between April and September. Always pack rainwear alongside light cotton clothing and a warm cover-up for visiting the highlands.

Paramaribo
Alt: 5m (16ft)

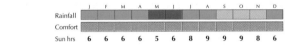

	J	F	M	A	M	J	J	A	S	O	N	D
Rainfall												
Comfort												
Sun hrs	6	6	6	6	5	6	8	9	9	9	8	6

Climate   **Tropical Equatorial**

Swaziland

Capital City: Mbabane World Map ref: **F6** (In southern hemisphere)

This tiny country comprises both highlands (or high veld) and lowlands and weather patterns vary accordingly. The high veld has a temperate climate with substantial rain (October to April). To the east, the country descends to lowlands where subtropical conditions prevail and, from October to April, the environment can be unpleasantly hot and humid. Take light clothes and waterproofs during the rainy months and pile in warmer clothing for the high veld.

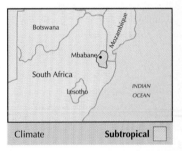

Mbabane
Alt: 1,155m (3,800ft)

	J	F	M	A	M	J	J	A	S	O	N	D
Rainfall												
Comfort												
Sun hrs	8	8	8	7	8	8	8	9	9	8	7	8

Climate   **Subtropical**

Sweden

Capital City: Stockholm World Map ref: **F1**

When planning a trip to Sweden, consider carefully which parts of the country you plan to visit: weather conditions vary considerably from north to south. In the hilly north and northwest, winters are bitterly cold and you'll find snow on the peaks throughout the year. Summer weather is changeable: you'll see more sunshine and less rain if you stay in the sheltered valleys. Northeast, on lower ground, the summers are even more balmy despite the region's proximity to the Arctic Circle. However, winter brings long periods of snow which can last more than four months.
In central and southern Sweden, winters are shorter but just as chilling as those in the north; summers are long and fairly warm, with little rain. Spring and autumn are the rainiest periods here and, in the winter, the rain turns to heavy snow, so go prepared. Even in summer, you should supplement light clothing with warmer attire so you can layer up. Wrap up very warmly for a winter visit.

Stockholm
Alt: 45m (150ft)

	J	F	M	A	M	J	J	A	S	O	N	D
Rainfall												
Comfort												
Sun hrs	1	3	5	7	9	11	10	8	6	3	1	1

Climate   **Continental**

Subarctic

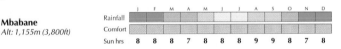

Cold but tolerable	Hot but tolerable	Danger of Heatstroke
Extremely Cold	Comfortable, Temperate	Hot & Sticky, Very Hot

Key to Comfort

Switzerland

Capital City: **Berne**   World Map ref: **E2**

Although a small country, Switzerland has a varied climate because of its mountains. Higher peaks are covered in snow for most of the year while the valleys enjoy warm but wet summers. The warmest part of the country is the lakeland district around Lakes Lugano and Maggiore, a beautiful, if rainy, place for a summer break. Central Switzerland, where most of the country's inhabitants live, is a low-lying area flanked by Lakes Geneva and Konstanz and it can fall prey to very severe winters. Summers, however, are warm if very wet with frequent thunderstorms.

Higher up, in the Jura Mountains, it is even rainier and summer days tend to be marred by cloud, while winters can be freezing in the valleys. The Swiss Alps, which lie between Geneva and Austria, are a good place to be in the winter provided you go high up: mountain conditions can be sunny and bright, if crisp, while the valleys below tend to be shrouded in cloud and fog. One thing, of which skiers should be wary, is the arrival of the Föhn, a warm southerly wind which raises temperatures very quickly and can spark avalanches. In the summer, cloud and mist surround the Alpine mountain tops so the warm and sunny valleys are the best place to be.

▥ Always be prepared for rain in Switzerland, especially in the lakeland district. Complement summer lightweights with warm jackets and wrap up well in the winter. Take skiwear for the mountains.

Climate   **Continental**
High Mountain & Plateau

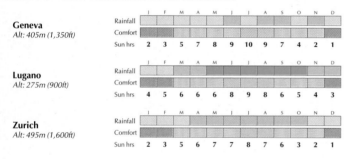

Geneva
Alt: 405m (1,350ft)

	J	F	M	A	M	J	J	A	S	O	N	D
Rainfall												
Comfort												
Sun hrs	2	3	5	7	8	9	10	9	7	4	2	1

Lugano
Alt: 275m (900ft)

	J	F	M	A	M	J	J	A	S	O	N	D
Rainfall												
Comfort												
Sun hrs	4	5	6	6	6	8	9	8	6	5	4	3

Zurich
Alt: 495m (1,600ft)

	J	F	M	A	M	J	J	A	S	O	N	D
Rainfall												
Comfort												
Sun hrs	2	3	5	6	7	7	8	7	6	3	2	1

Syria

Capital City: **Damascus**   World Map ref: **F3**

Syria's climate is a strange hybrid of influences from the Mediterranean and Arabian desert. The hottest part of the country is the desert land to the east which makes up more than half of Syria's surface. This is a region of extremes: baking hot summers, cold, frosty and even snowy winters and a rain pattern which, although sporadic, can bring dramatic localised flash floods. To the north and west lie plains which are as hot as the desert region but have higher rainfall. Mountains lie between these plains and the Mediterranean and, on high ground, both rainfall and snow cover can be substantial. The coast is hot and muggy in the summer and mild and wet with spells of fine weather in the winter months. The beginning and end of the summer can see the dramatic arrival of the hot and dusty Khamsin winds which can send temperatures soaring as high as 48°C (118°F). ▥ Take light clothes in the summer with scarves for protection against heat and dust. In winter, warm clothing is needed when travelling inland to the mountains or the desert. Anticipate winter rain if you are staying on the coast.

Climate   **Hot Desert**   **Steppe**
Mediterranean
High Mountain & Plateau

Damascus
Alt: 720m (2,350ft)

	J	F	M	A	M	J	J	A	S	O	N	D
Rainfall												
Comfort												
Sun hrs	5	6	7	9	10	12	13	12	10	8	7	5

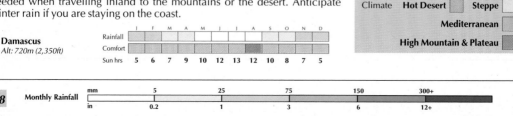

	mm	5	25	75	150	300+
Monthly Rainfall	in	0.2	1	3	6	12+

Taiwan

Capital City: **Taipei**   World Map ref: **I3**

Taiwan, which lies off the coast of China, is a mountainous island with lowlands in its west. It is a land of hot, rainy summers and pleasantly cool but rainy winters. The heaviest rains fall between June and October when Taiwan is frequently hit by typhoons blowing in from the South China Sea and bringing high winds and torrential downpours in their wake. In northern Taiwan, poor weather continues into the winter months, when heavy cloud and rain frequently engulf the coasts, bringing lower temperatures than on the much sunnier south of the island. 👕 Take light clothing to alleviate the hot, humid summer conditions, mixing in warmer wear if you are travelling in the autumn or winter. Always go prepared for rain.

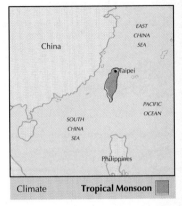

Taipei
Alt: 10m (35ft)

	J	F	M	A	M	J	J	A	S	O	N	D
Rainfall												
Comfort												
Sun hrs	3	3	3	4	5	6	7	7	6	5	3	3

Climate   **Tropical Monsoon**

Tajikistan

Capital City: **Dushanbe**   World Map ref: **G3**

This is a very mountainous country of which more than half lies above 3,000m (10,000ft). Its southwest has very hot, dry summers but in winter there is a wind chill factor from hell which sends temperatures plummeting. 👕 In the summer, supplement light clothes with warmer wraps when travelling to higher ground. Take very warm clothes (including scarves and hats) for the winter months.

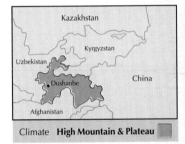

Dushanbe
Alt: 800m (2,600ft)   No weather statistics are available for this location

Climate   **High Mountain & Plateau**

Tanzania

Capital City: **Dar-es-Salaam**   World Map ref: **F5**   (In southern hemisphere)

This is the biggest country in East Africa and it has a varied topography ranging from a long coastline to hill districts and mountains. Its highest point, Mount Kilimanjaro, is always covered with snow but, elsewhere, a tropical climate prevails with hot temperatures and high humidity, especially on the coast. The main rainy season is from November to May. 👕 The higher you go in Tanzania, the lower the temperature, especially at night, so take warm clothes if you are planning a trip to the highlands. On the coast, light clothing is fine even if you are travelling between June and September when the weather is cooler and less humid. Be prepared for showers at any time on the sea shore.

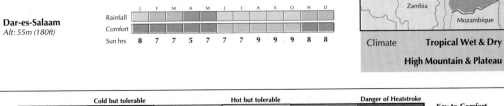

Dar-es-Salaam
Alt: 55m (180ft)

	J	F	M	A	M	J	J	A	S	O	N	D
Rainfall												
Comfort												
Sun hrs	8	7	7	5	7	7	7	9	9	9	8	8

Climate   **Tropical Wet & Dry**

High Mountain & Plateau

Thailand

Capital City: **Bangkok**   World Map ref: **H4**

This is a great winter sun destination. From November to February, you'll find the country at its best with dry, sunny weather prevailing but cooler evenings in Chiang Mai and the northern hilly region. After February, the weather grows much hotter and more sultry in the run up to the monsoon rains which start in May and last until October. These bring a level of humidity which, combined with the heat, gives the atmosphere the feeling of a wet blanket. The far south, which includes Phuket, tends to have a longer rainy season than the rest of Thailand. ▦ Take light clothes with something warmer for winter nights in the north and rainwear in the wet season.

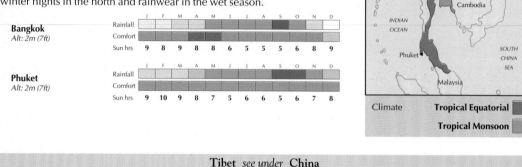

Bangkok Alt: 2m (7ft)	J	F	M	A	M	J	J	A	S	O	N	D
Rainfall												
Comfort												
Sun hrs	9	8	9	8	8	6	5	5	5	6	8	9

Phuket Alt: 2m (7ft)	J	F	M	A	M	J	J	A	S	O	N	D
Rainfall												
Comfort												
Sun hrs	9	10	9	8	7	5	6	6	5	6	7	8

Climate   **Tropical Equatorial** ▨

Tropical Monsoon ▨

Tibet *see under* China

Togo

Capital City: **Lomé**   World Map ref: **E4**

Like Ghana, Togo has more rain inland than on its coast because of cold currents off its short coastline. The north of the country sees comparatively little rain in its summer rainy season, while the south has rains from March to July and again in October. The best time to go is between November and February when humidity abates and sunshine abounds. ▦ Pack light clothing and add waterproofs if travelling in the south during the rainy season.

Lomé Alt: 20m (65ft)	J	F	M	A	M	J	J	A	S	O	N	D
Rainfall												
Comfort												
Sun hrs	7	8	7	7	7	5	4	4	5	7	8	8

Climate   **Tropical Equatorial** ▨

Tropical Wet & Dry ▨

Tonga

Capital City: **Nuku'alofa**   World Map ref: **J5**   (In southern hemisphere)

Tonga comprises three groups of islands which lie southeast of Fiji. The largest island, Tongatapu, is mountainous and strong sea breezes keep temperatures a little cooler than in most tropical climes. There is some rain all year but December to April are the hottest, wettest and most humid months. ▦ Pack light clothes with warmer wraps for the evenings and mountain trips. Be prepared for rain at any time of year.

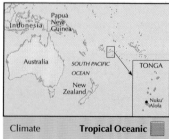

Nuku'alofa Alt: 5m (16ft)	J	F	M	A	M	J	J	A	S	O	N	D
Rainfall												
Comfort												
Sun hrs	6	7	5	5	5	5	5	5	5	7	7	8

Climate   **Tropical Oceanic** ▨

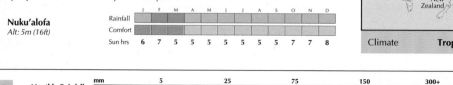

Monthly Rainfall							
mm		5	25	75	150	300+	
in		0.2	1	3	6	12+	

Trinidad & Tobago

Capital City: **Port-of-Spain, Trinidad**   World Map ref: **C4**

These are the most southerly of the Caribbean islands and Trinidad, in particular, shares its climate with the northeast coast of Venezuela which lies very near to it. This makes it hotter than more northerly islands although Trinidad's southerly position puts it out of the way of the hurricanes and tropical storms which plague other parts of the Caribbean. Rain falls on Trinidad and Tobago throughout the year but it is most intense between June and November when temperatures reach their peak. However, stickiness is tempered by refreshing northeast trade winds. 🌦 Take light cotton clothing for any time of year.

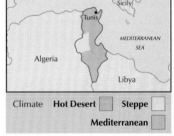

Trinidad
Alt: 12m (40ft)

	J	F	M	A	M	J	J	A	S	O	N	D
Rainfall												
Comfort												
Sun hrs	7	8	8	8	8	6	7	7	7	7	7	7

Climate   **Tropical Oceanic**

Tunisia

Capital City: **Tunis**   World Map ref: **F3**

Although only about the size of England, Tunisia has a coast as well as desert and mountains and its weather conditions are as varied as its topography. The Mediterranean coastline basks in hot summers and warm winters and rain is likely in the spring and autumn months. There is more rain (and even occasional snowfall) in the mountains but, in central Tunisia, rainfall is lower and temperatures more extreme, both in the summer and winter, than on the coast. In the south, the country reverts to desert with searing hot days, chilly nights and little rain. 🌦 Take light clothing for the summer months and warmer wear for the winter. Be prepared for cold nights in the southern desert.

Tunis
Alt: 3m (10ft)

	J	F	M	A	M	J	J	A	S	O	N	D
Rainfall												
Comfort												
Sun hrs	5	6	7	8	10	11	12	11	9	7	6	5

Climate   **Hot Desert**   **Steppe**

Mediterranean

Turkey

Capital City: **Ankara**   World Map ref: **F3**

Part of Turkey is in Europe but the bulk of it, Anatolia, lies in Asia. Anatolia is a high plateau with mountains to its east, north and south. The higher peaks draw snow throughout the year and the climate here contrasts with that of lower ground and coastal regions to give Turkey a wide variety of weather conditions. The country's interior has a hot, arid summer climate and cold winters which increase in harshness the further east you go. The coasts bordering the Black Sea, the Aegean and the Mediterranean have higher rainfall and warmer winters. Even between the coasts, however, conditions can vary. The area surrounding Istanbul and the Black Sea is slightly colder in winter and rainier throughout the year than the shorelines to the west and south whose weather is more typically Mediterranean and can be hot and sticky on summer nights. The hottest part of Turkey is the wide plain which borders Syria at the entrance to the Taurus Mountains. Here, you'll find a desert-like climate with fiercely hot summers and cold winters.
🌦 Light clothes are fine in the summer months, but in winter take very warm clothes for visiting the interior or the mountains.

Istanbul
Alt: 115m (380ft)

	J	F	M	A	M	J	J	A	S	O	N	D
Rainfall												
Comfort												
Sun hrs	3	4	4	6	9	11	12	11	8	6	4	3

Climate   **Steppe**

Mediterranean

High Mountain & Plateau

Cold but tolerable		Hot but tolerable		Danger of Heatstroke	
Extremely Cold		Comfortable, Temperate		Hot & Sticky, Very Hot	

Key to Comfort

Turkmenistan

Capital City: **Ashkhabad**   World Map ref: **G3**

The Kara-Kum "Black Sands" desert occupies most of this country, so brace yourself for severe extremes of temperature. In the summer, Turkmenistan bakes in temperatures as high as 45°C (113°F), while winter can bring them down to the minus 10s. There is a sharp difference between daytime and night time temperatures. ▣ Take light clothing for the summer with warm wraps for desert nights. A winter visit requires very heavy clothing with sturdy hats and warm scarves to keep out the wind.

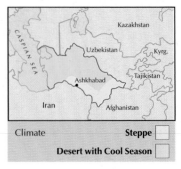

Ashkhabad
Alt: 225m (740ft)

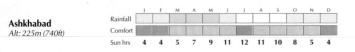

	J	F	M	A	M	J	J	A	S	O	N	D
Rainfall												
Comfort												
Sun hrs	4	4	5	7	9	11	12	11	10	8	5	4

Climate   **Steppe** ☐

Desert with Cool Season ☐

Turks & Caicos Islands

Capital City: **Cockburn Town, Grand Turk**   World Map ref: **C3**

This group of 30 islands lie at the southeastern end of the Bahamas chain. Don't book into the largest island, Grand Caicos, as it's uninhabited! Rainfall is light for the Caribbean: the wettest months are from September to November although there is the chance of tropical storms or hurricanes between July and November. The Turks and Caicos are consistently hot throughout the year but trade winds temper humidity to create a balmy, pleasant environment. ▣ Pack lightweight clothes, beachwear and take cover-ups for winter evenings which can be chilly.

Grand Turk
Alt: 8m (25ft)

	J	F	M	A	M	J	J	A	S	O	N	D
Rainfall												
Comfort												
Sun hrs	7	8	9	9	9	8	9	9	7	7	7	7

Climate   **Tropical Oceanic** ▨

Uganda

Capital City: **Kampala**   World Map ref: **F4**

Although it is landlocked, Uganda's weather is affected by the presence of three huge lakes: Lake Victoria, Lake Kioga and Lake Albert. Lake Victoria, in particular, generates belts of heavy rain and thunderstorms which affect the lake shore and the Western mountains. Central and northern Uganda have less rain. The rest of the country has two main rainy seasons - March to May and October to December - when downpours can be heavy and apparently endless. Uganda is a high country and its altitude creates temperate conditions with humidity under control and plenty of sunshine away from the mountains. ▣ Nights can be cool, so supplement light clothing with warmer attire. Take effective waterproofing if travelling during the rainy seasons.

Kampala
Alt: 1,145m (3,800ft)

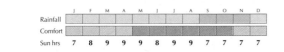

	J	F	M	A	M	J	J	A	S	O	N	D
Rainfall												
Comfort												
Sun hrs	5	6	5	4	4	6	6	5	5	5	5	4

Climate   **Tropical Wet & Dry** ▨

	mm	5	25	75	150	300+
Monthly Rainfall	in	0.2	1	3	6	12+

Ukraine

Capital City: **Kiev**   World Map ref: **F2**

The Ukraine, which lies to the southwest of European Russia and has a Black Sea coast, has warm but wet summers with up to 10 hours of sunshine per day. Winters are bitingly cold, especially when the harsh winds from Siberia blow. An exception is the Crimean peninsular on the Black Sea which has milder winters, but these warmer conditions are marred by extremely heavy rain. Take light clothes in the summer. Mix in warmer clothes for spring and autumn visits and wrap up heavily to brave the winter months. Always be prepared for rain.

Kiev
Alt: 165m (540ft)

	J	F	M	A	M	J	J	A	S	O	N	D
Rainfall												
Comfort												
Sun hrs	1	2	4	6	9	9	10	8	7	5	2	1

Climate   **Steppe**

Continental

United Arab Emirates

Capital City: **Abu Dhabi**   World Map ref: **G3**

Unless you would enjoy living in a sauna, avoid visiting the United Arab Emirates between mid-May and September. At this time, the fierce sun is at its most unforgiving and there is a serious risk of heatstroke for the unwary. During the rest of the year, a visit to the UAE can be a great pleasure: from mid-October to April, the climate is warm and sunny with sparse and sporadic rainfall. Take light clothes, whatever the time of year, and warmer wraps to combat the winter weather, summer air-conditioning and evenings in the inland desert which can grow chilly.

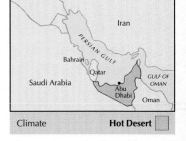

Abu Dhabi
Alt: 5m (16ft)

	J	F	M	A	M	J	J	A	S	O	N	D
Rainfall												
Comfort												
Sun hrs	9	10	9	11	12	12	9	10	11	10	10	9

Climate   **Hot Desert**

United Kingdom

Capital City: **London**   World Map ref: **E2**

No wonder the British are obsessed with the weather: they have one of the world's most changeable climates. The general pattern is for summers to be warm and wet and winters to be cool and wet. However, the quirky weather can leave the islands basking in sunshine as hot as the Mediterranean's during a good summer and shivering in temperatures as cold as Moscow's during a particularly harsh winter.

In the UK, weather conditions vary widely from day to day and from region to region. The southwest is the warmest area while the west coast and the mountains attract the most rain. The east coast is generally a chilly and blustery region with colder winters than other areas. London and the southeast enjoy more periods of sunshine and are drier and warmer than the north.

The mountains of Scotland, Wales and northern England can be treacherous. In the summer months, they can record some of the highest rainfall in Europe while, in winter, they are prone to blizzards, gales and icy rain. Unwary mountain walkers frequently have to be rescued when a sudden turn in the weather leaves them stranded and in danger of frostbite or worse.

Scotland, because of its northerly latitude, experiences longer days in the summer and shorter days in the winter than anywhere else in the UK but, as a rule, temperatures there are no lower than in England. The west of the

Climate   **Maritime**

	Cold but tolerable		Hot but tolerable		Danger of Heatstroke	
Extremely Cold		Comfortable, Temperate		Hot & Sticky, Very Hot		

Key to Comfort

United Kingdom - *continued*

country is warmer and rainier than the east and visitors exploring the Highlands should be prepared for sudden fog and mists.

Wales is generally less sunny and more rainy than England but its coasts can enjoy prolonged periods of sunshine in the summer and are therefore popular with tourists. The Welsh Mountains should be approached with respect at any time of year as conditions can quickly turn nasty.

Northern Ireland suffers highly changeable weather conditions and tends to be wetter with less sun than other parts of the UK.

Always bring a range of clothing when touring Britain. Layered clothing, which can be added to or removed according to temperature and conditions, is probably the best bet. Expect the odd short sharp shower and, if in the Lake District or the mountains, rainwear is recommended.

London *Alt: 5m (16ft)*		J	F	M	A	M	J	J	A	S	O	N	D
	Rainfall												
	Comfort												
	Sun hrs	1	2	4	5	6	7	6	6	5	3	2	1

Edinburgh *Alt: 135m (440ft)*		J	F	M	A	M	J	J	A	S	O	N	D
	Rainfall												
	Comfort												
	Sun hrs	2	3	4	5	6	6	5	4	4	3	2	1

United States

Capital City: **Washington**   World Map ref: **A3-C3**

The weather in the world's fourth largest country is as varied as its inhabitants. For ease of reference, we have divided the United States into climatic regions running from East to West.

The Northeastern States

This region contains lovely New England, the states of Maine, Rhode Island, New Hampshire, Connecticut, Vermont and Massachusetts, as well as New Jersey, Maryland, Delaware, the eastern parts of Pennsylvania and New York State and the District of Columbia with America's capital, Washington. Throughout this region the weather is changeable and there can be rain at any time of year. The northern parts experience wet, snowy winters while, further south, the summer is the main season for rainfall. Both summer and winter conditions can be extreme: New York is a typical example of the blazing summer heatspells and bitterly cold winters which can afflict the region. The Appalachian Mountains receive heavy winter snows on their upper reaches which contain popular ski resorts. In the summer, the mountain resorts are a cool sanctuary from the heat and humidity of the cities and the coast. Pack light clothes for a summer visit to this part of the States. Wrap up much more warmly in the winter and always have layers of light and warmer clothing at hand for any season since temperatures can vary from day to day.

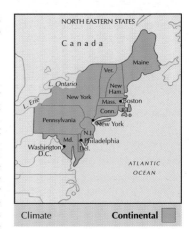

Climate   **Continental**

Boston *Alt: 6m (20ft)*		J	F	M	A	M	J	J	A	S	O	N	D
	Rainfall												
	Comfort												
	Sun hrs	5	6	7	7	9	10	11	9	8	7	5	5

New York *Alt: 4m (13ft)*		J	F	M	A	M	J	J	A	S	O	N	D
	Rainfall												
	Comfort												
	Sun hrs	5	6	7	7	8	10	10	9	8	7	6	5

Washington *Alt: 20m (65ft)*		J	F	M	A	M	J	J	A	S	O	N	D
	Rainfall												
	Comfort												
	Sun hrs	5	6	7	8	9	9	9	8	8	7	5	4

> Weather Statistics for 315 locations around the world
> *see pages 94-103*

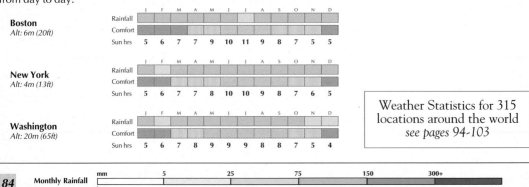

Monthly Rainfall	mm	5	25	75	150	300+
	in	0.2	1	3	6	12+

The Southern Atlantic States

Georgia, North and South Carolina, Florida, Virginia and West Virginia all lie in this region which ranges from being mountainous and cold-wintered in the north to almost tropical in the south. While the Appalachian mountain ranges of Virginia and West Virginia have cold, snowy winters, Florida basks in balmy warmth which has made it a top destination for holidaymakers and retired people. In the summer, north and south experience similar temperatures but summers are longer in the south. On the other hand, the more southern states experience much more rain, often in the shape of ferocious thunderstorms with the result that summers tend to be less sunny and more humid here than in the states further north. Florida can also fall prey to hurricanes and tropical storms during the months from July to October. ◼▶ Take very warm clothing if you are visiting Virginia or West Virginia in the winter. In Florida you can get away with light to medium gear. Light clothing with a few warmer cover-ups are fine in the summer, but you should pay attention to storm warnings.

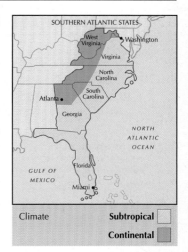

Climate   **Subtropical**

Continental

Miami
Alt: 3m (10ft)

	J	F	M	A	M	J	J	A	S	O	N	D
Rainfall												
Comfort												
Sun hrs	8	8	9	9	9	9	9	8	7	6	7	7

The South & Gulf States

Arkansas, Oklahoma, Texas, Louisiana, Tennessee, Alabama and Mississippi make up the vast southern interior of America, a region which has similar weather patterns to the Midwest but is warmed by its more southerly location and access to tropical currents of air coming in from Atlantic and the Gulf of Mexico. This means that winters are shorter and much milder, temperatures rarely falling below freezing point except when Arctic winds howl down from the north bringing short, intense cold snaps as far south as Texas. Summers are long and warm and there are more pronounced spring and autumn seasons. The east of the region is much rainier than the west and witnesses frequent summer storms, but summer can bring rain to the whole area. The snowiest parts of the region in winter are the mountainous areas of Alabama and Tennessee which contain the Southern Appalachians. Overall, this region has a very sunny climate, clocking up an average of 6 daily hours of sunshine in the winter and 10 in the summer. The heat is largely dry except on the coast of the Mexican Gulf where high humidity can make midsummer tiresome and hurricanes can hit between July and October. ◼▶ Take light clothes and be prepared for rain in the summer, and pack reasonably warm clothing in the winter months.

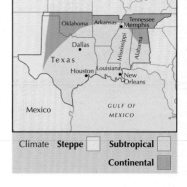

Climate **Steppe**   **Subtropical**

Continental

New Orleans
Alt: 9m (30ft)

	J	F	M	A	M	J	J	A	S	O	N	D
Rainfall												
Comfort												
Sun hrs	5	6	7	8	9	9	8	8	8	8	6	5

The American Midwest

This region stretches from the Appalachians to the Rocky Mountains and comprises the states of Minnesota, Illinois, Kansas, Ohio, Kentucky, Missouri, Indiana, North and South Dakota, Wisconsin, Michigan, Nebraska and Iowa. It contains vast tracts of open prairie and has the most typically Continental climate to be found in the US: hot, dry summers and severe winters. Winters are most severe in the northern states and summers are hottest in those to the south. States to the east - Michigan, Indiana, Illinois and Kentucky - have heavier rainfall throughout the year than those in the west. Winter is an exciting time to visit the American Midwest as the locals organise plenty of activities, like snowmobiling, skiing and ice fishing, to stop themselves going "cabin crazy". The weather, although cold, is predominantly sunny and bright, producing some Christmas card scenes. However, in the northern states, you should be careful on the winter roads: freezing rain turns highways into ice rinks for days at a time. Another hazard in the spring and early summer are "twisters", aptly named violent but

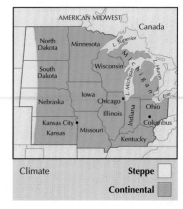

Climate   **Steppe**

Continental

Cold but tolerable		Hot but tolerable		Danger of Heatstroke	
Extremely Cold	**Comfortable, Temperate**		**Hot & Sticky, Very Hot**		

Key to Comfort

United States - *continued*

localised tornados which can cause severe damage to property and people in their path. 🧳 Take light clothing in the summer (with a warm wrap for chilly evenings) and much cosier, ski-style clothes in the winter. Anticipate rain in the eastern states.

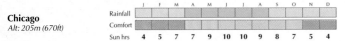

Chicago Alt: 205m (670ft)	J	F	M	A	M	J	J	A	S	O	N	D
Rainfall												
Comfort												
Sun hrs	4	5	7	7	9	10	10	9	8	7	5	4

The Rocky Mountain States

These include Wyoming, Idaho, Montana, Utah, Colorado, Nevada, New Mexico and Arizona which are home to some of America's most well-known ski resorts. The three northern states, Wyoming, Idaho and Montana, have a cooler climate in the winter and summer than the rest; they also experience more rain and have a longer winter. However, there are huge variations of weather in this mountainous region. The south is light on rainfall and very sunny. Vast areas of Colorado, Utah, New Mexico and Arizona are desert or semi-desert and summer temperatures can soar very high, although the heat is dry and therefore more bearable than it would be in a humid climate. Conversely, winter temperatures in the northern states can plunge very low indeed. 🧳 Take light clothing for the summer, unless heading for the northern states when these should be supplemented with warmer cover-ups and rainwear. In winter there is a high wind chill factor in the Rockies, so skiers should go prepared.

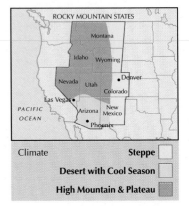

Las Vegas Alt: 660m (2,150ft)	J	F	M	A	M	J	J	A	S	O	N	D
Rainfall												
Comfort												
Sun hrs	8	9	10	11	12	14	12	12	12	10	9	10

Phoenix Alt: 345m (1,150ft)	J	F	M	A	M	J	J	A	S	O	N	D
Rainfall												
Comfort												
Sun hrs	8	10	11	12	13	14	13	12	12	10	9	9

Climate   **Steppe** ☐
Desert with Cool Season ☐
High Mountain & Plateau ☐

California

This state deserves a mention all to itself because of its unusual Mediterranean-style climate which gets warmer and drier the further south you go. The state's extreme southeast witnesses hardly any rainfall and conditions are semi-desert with temperatures soaring in the summer months: the aptly named Death Valley records some of the highest temperatures in the world! The coast, where San Diego, San Francisco and Los Angeles are situated, has coolish summers with frequent fog and mild, rainy winters. Rain also falls heavily in the Sierra Nevada range and the mountains which back the coast; this turns to snow on the higher peaks and gives California its reputation as a place where you can ski in the morning and sunbathe in the afternoon. You should, however, take care in the mountains as sudden, heavy snowstorms can occur. Another climatic hazard is urban smog around Los Angeles which is a mixture of fog and pollution trapped by a blanket of coastal warm air. However, overall, California is a delightful place to visit and deserves its nickname "the sunshine state". 🧳 Take light clothes for visiting south California in the summer, add a few wraps if you are going to the coast and much warmer clothes for trips to the mountains. Take fairly warm clothing in the winter when you should be prepared for the occasional cold snap, and rain.

Los Angeles Alt: 40m (130ft)	J	F	M	A	M	J	J	A	S	O	N	D
Rainfall												
Comfort												
Sun hrs	7	8	9	9	9	10	12	11	10	9	8	8

San Francisco Alt: 6m (20ft)	J	F	M	A	M	J	J	A	S	O	N	D
Rainfall												
Comfort												
Sun hrs	5	7	8	10	11	11	10	9	9	8	7	6

Climate   **Desert with Cool Season** ☐
Mediterranean ☐
High Mountain & Plateau ☐

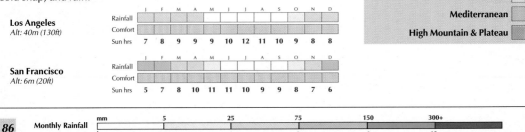

mm	5	25	75	150	300+
in	0.2	1	3	6	12+

United States - *continued*

The Pacific Northwest

This is the closest you'll get to finding British-style weather across the Atlantic. The region holds the states of Washington and Oregon, both of which are mountainous. In their higher reaches, the mountains are covered in snow all year and winters are sunny but crisp with some snow. Summers are rainy. On the coast at Portland and Seattle you'll find weather that reminds you of Britain: drizzly and cloudy but mild in the winter and fairly warm but foggy and changeable in the summer. Both summers and winters are sunnier inland.  Take British-style clothes for this climate: warmish attire with rainwear for the summer and much heavier wear for visiting the mountains or travelling in the winter months.

Seattle
Alt: 5m (16ft)

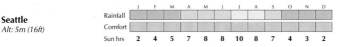

	J	F	M	A	M	J	J	A	S	O	N	D
Rainfall												
Comfort												
Sun hrs	2	4	5	7	8	8	10	8	7	4	3	2

Climate   **Maritime**

High Mountain & Plateau

Alaska

The largest of the American states is a popular haunt for cruise ships in the summer months when people flock from all over the world to view its wildlife and dramatic glaciers. Much of the state is mountainous, hence those glaciers, but there are broad lowlands in the interior which, together with the north coast, have an Arctic or subarctic climate of permanent snow and ice. Summers in Alaska, although short, are surprisingly warm: cruise passengers sit on deck in shirtsleeves taking photographs of icebergs! However, rain can be very heavy in the summer along the coast. Winters everywhere in Alaska are long, dark and severe but conditions are milder on the coast than inland. Whenever you go, be prepared for cloudy, foggy days.  Take light to medium clothes in the summer with sturdy boots and effective waterproofs. In winter, take the works: thermal underwear, windproof and waterproof clothing, warm hats, gloves and boots, scarves and earmuffs as the winter wind chill can be a killer.

Anchorage
Alt: 60m (200ft)

	J	F	M	A	M	J	J	A	S	O	N	D
Rainfall												
Comfort												
Sun hrs	2	3	6	9	8	10	8	6	4	3	2	2

Climate   **Maritime**   **Icecap**

Subarctic

High Mountain & Plateau

The Hawaiian Islands

These mountainous islands, America's 50th state, lie in the centre of the Pacific Ocean, five hours' flying time from mainland United States. Their tropical oceanic climate, tempered by trade winds, has combined with spectacular scenery and colourful traditions to create phenomenal growth in tourism over the past three decades. The south and west coasts of the islands (where most holiday resorts are located) receive a lot of sunshine and little rain throughout the year. Although there is a rainy season from December to March, this is the high season for tourism! On the islands' mountainous northeast coasts it's a different story: these are exposed to the full force of the Pacific trade winds and experience much heavier rainfall. Kauai's mountains house one of the wettest places on earth. Cyclones can hit the islands from May to November but these are comparatively rare. Temperatures are high throughout the year but never excessive and humidity levels are low. 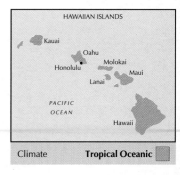 Pack light clothes with cover-ups for the winter months.

Climate   **Tropical Oceanic**

Honolulu
Alt: 2m (7ft)

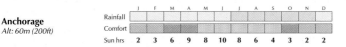

	J	F	M	A	M	J	J	A	S	O	N	D
Rainfall												
Comfort												
Sun hrs	7	8	9	9	10	10	11	11	9	8	6	7

World Climate Map
see pages 6-7

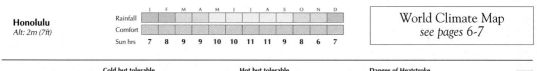

Cold but tolerable	Hot but tolerable	Danger of Heatstroke	**Key to Comfort**
Extremely Cold	Comfortable, Temperate	Hot & Sticky, Very Hot	

Uruguay

Capital City: **Montevideo**　World Map ref: **D6**　(In southern hemisphere)

Uruguay, which lies on the east coast of South America between Argentina and Brazil, is a low-lying and largely flat country. It has a healthy and pleasant subtropical climate similar to that of the Argentinian pampas region with little variation between inland weather and weather on the coast although temperatures are slightly higher in the interior. Rainfall is moderate but you can expect at least one downpour a week at any time of the year. In the summer months (November to March), temperatures are never excessive and there is an average of 10 sunshine hours a day. Winters are mild and frost and snow are virtually unheard of. 🧳 Take light clothes with a few cover-ups for the summer and medium to warm wear in the winter. Evenings can be chilly at any time of year, so be prepared.

Montevideo
Alt: 20m (65ft)

	J	F	M	A	M	J	J	A	S	O	N	D
Rainfall												
Comfort												
Sun hrs	11	10	9	8	6	5	5	6	7	8	10	10

Climate　　**Subtropical** ☐

Uzbekistan

Capital City: **Tashkent**　World Map ref: **G2**

Samarkand, on the ancient "silk road", lies in central Uzbekistan and has desert to its north and west and higher ground to the south and east. Temperatures are extreme with very hot summers and bitterly cold winters. If you must go in the winter, the south is marginally less cold than the north. 🧳 Take light clothes for a summer visit, supplemented by warmer wear for the evenings. Wrap up very warmly in the winter and be prepared for rain between October and May.

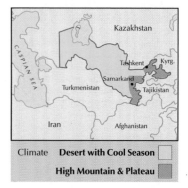

Tashkent
Alt: 480m (1,550ft)

	J	F	M	A	M	J	J	A	S	O	N	D
Rainfall												
Comfort												
Sun hrs	4	4	5	8	10	12	13	12	10	8	5	4

Climate　　**Desert with Cool Season** ☐

High Mountain & Plateau ☐

Vanuatu

Capital City: **Port-Vila**　World Map ref: **J5**　(In southern hemisphere)

Vanuatu comprises 70 islands which are densely forested and mountainous. November to April are the hottest months but also the most humid and the time of heavy rainfall and occasional cyclones. From May to October the weather is hot and sunny and trade winds bring refreshing breezes. 🧳 Pack light clothes if you are planning a visit.

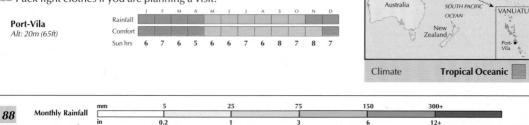

Port-Vila
Alt: 20m (65ft)

	J	F	M	A	M	J	J	A	S	O	N	D
Rainfall												
Comfort												
Sun hrs	6	7	6	5	6	6	7	6	8	7	8	7

Climate　　**Tropical Oceanic** ☐

mm		5	25	75	150	300+
in		0.2	1	3	6	12+

Venezuela

Capital City: **Caracas**   World Map ref: **C4**

In the north of Venezuela, there is a long narrow Caribbean coastal plain rising up to the Andes Mountains. The central plains (known as the Llanos) follow the valleys of the Orinoco river and, to the southeast, the land rises to an extensive plateau, the Guyana Highlands. Venezuela is unusual amongst South American countries in that its main rainy season falls between April and October. In the Llanos region, however, you should go prepared for downpours at any time of year when high temperatures and humidity make conditions muggy and oppressive. The northern slopes of the Andes and Venezuela's northeastern coastal lowlands are the driest parts of the country. On the high peaks of the Andes, rain falls as snow and temperatures can be very cold, especially at night. In the southeastern highlands rainfall is high during the wet season but temperatures are crisp and conditions delightful during the dry season. The best time to visit Venezuela is from January to April when rainfall is at its lowest in all parts of the country.

Pack light cotton clothes for the coast and the Llanos. Take warm to heavy clothes if you are going to the hills or up into the Andes.

Climate	**Tropical Equatorial**
	Tropical Wet & Dry
	High Mountain & Plateau

Caracas
Alt: 1,040m (3,400ft)

	J	F	M	A	M	J	J	A	S	O	N	D
Rainfall												
Comfort												
Sun hrs	8	9	8	7	6	7	8	8	7	7	7	7

Vietnam

Capital City: **Hanoi**   World Map ref: **I4**

Vietnam, which is now attracting more and more visitors, is a tropical country with a typical monsoon climate. Most of the country has one rainy season from May to September when humidity is at its highest and conditions can be sultry and oppressive. Outside these months, much of Vietnam is virtually dry. Exceptions to this are parts of the central highlands which experience most of their rain between September and January. The south of Vietnam is warmest and sunniest during the dry winter months. In the north, there is very little sun and cold fronts blowing in from China reduce temperatures. Take light clothing, rainwear during the monsoon season and warmer clothing if you are going north or up into the mountains during the winter.

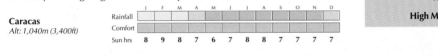

Ho Chi Minh City
Alt: 10m (35ft)

	J	F	M	A	M	J	J	A	S	O	N	D
Rainfall												
Comfort												
Sun hrs	5	6	5	6	4	4	5	5	4	4	4	

Climate	**Tropical Monsoon**

Virgin Islands

Capital City: **Road Town, Charlotte Amalie**   World Map ref: **C4**

The Virgin Islands, the most northern of the Leewards, are a group of about 100 islands. They comprise the British Virgin Islands, of which the capital is Road Town on Tortola (of Treasure Island fame), and the US Virgin Islands, whose capital is Charlotte Amalie on St Thomas. Rainfall occurs throughout the year but is heaviest between July and November when tropical storms and hurricanes can hit. These islands are delightfully hot and sunny all year: easterly trade winds not only make them very popular with "yachties", they also please other holidaymakers by keeping humidity under control.

Pack light clothes with cover-ups for cooler winter evenings.

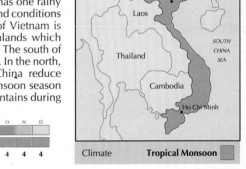

Tortola
Alt: 4m (13ft)

	J	F	M	A	M	J	J	A	S	O	N	D
Rainfall												
Comfort												
Sun hrs	8	8	10	9	9	8	9	9	7	8	7	7

Climate	**Tropical Oceanic**

Cold but tolerable		Hot but tolerable		Danger of Heatstroke	
Extremely Cold	**Comfortable, Temperate**		**Hot & Sticky, Very Hot**		**Key to Comfort**

Western Samoa

Capital City: **Apia** World Map ref: **J5** (In southern hemisphere)

The two main islands of Western Samoa are mountainous and attract heavy rains between November and April. Temperatures and humidity are consistently high all year but trade winds produce pleasant conditions between May and September. Pack light clothes and a cover-up for the evenings which can be a bit chilly.

Apia
Alt: 2m (7ft)

	J	F	M	A	M	J	J	A	S	O	N	D
Rainfall												
Comfort												
Sun hrs	6	6	6	6	7	7	7	7	8	6	6	6

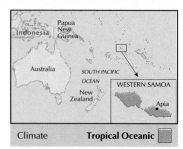

Climate   **Tropical Oceanic**

Yemen

Capital City: **San'a** World Map ref: **G4**

The climate of this small, mountainous country varies with altitude. Its Red Sea coast is hot and humid in the summer but experiences very little rain, and the mixture of extreme heat, sticky air and dust makes it an unpleasant place to be. Time a visit to the coast between November and March, if you can. Up in the mountains, the climate is much more temperate with rainfall sufficiently high to allow the cultivation of coffee beans and other crops. Summers are warm and rainy with strong sunshine but winter temperatures can fall very low. Take light clothes whatever the time of year if you are visiting the coast (remember head protection in the summer months). Supplement light to medium clothing with rainwear for visiting the mountains in the summer. You'll need very warm clothing if contemplating a winter trip into the Yemen highlands.

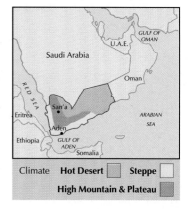

Climate   **Hot Desert**   **Steppe**

High Mountain & Plateau

Aden
Alt: 3m (10ft)

	J	F	M	A	M	J	J	A	S	O	N	D
Rainfall												
Comfort												
Sun hrs	11	10	9	10	9	10	7	8	10	11	10	10

Yugoslavia

Capital City: **Belgrade** World Map ref: **F2**

We have included under Yugoslavia the former Yugoslav Republics of Macedonia, Montenegro and Serbia.
Macedonia is a mountainous region with warm summers and cold winters. Heavy snows linger for a long time and can last through to the spring.
The coast of Montenegro has a Mediterranean-type climate with hot summers moderated by sea breezes and cloudy, wet winters. The inland mountain ranges are among the wettest places in Europe during the summer months and can attract heavy snows in winter.
Landlocked Serbia shares a climate with Eastern Europe - baking hot summers and howlingly cold winters - especially in the mountain regions where Alpine conditions prevail bringing heavy and long-lying snows. In the northern, low-lying Danube regions, there is little chance of rain but winters can be bitter. In the hot summers, light clothing is appropriate, particularly for the coast, but take something a little warmer for the evenings. In the winter, dress warmly and very much so if you are going into the mountains. Be prepared for rain whatever the season.

Climate   **Mediterranean**

Continental

Belgrade
Alt: 130m (430ft)

	J	F	M	A	M	J	J	A	S	O	N	D
Rainfall												
Comfort												
Sun hrs	2	3	5	6	7	9	10	9	8	3	3	2

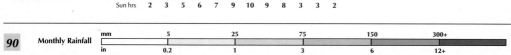

mm	5	25	75	150	300+
in	0.2	1	3	6	12+

Zaire – Democratic Republic of Congo

Capital City: **Kinshasa** World Map ref: **F5** (In southern hemisphere)

The Equator crosses the north of this country and gives its two distinct bands of weather. In the north, heavy rains occur between March and November while, in the south, the rains come between October and May. Areas close to the equator have two wet seasons and so, effectively, experience rain all year round. Surprisingly, Zaire's tiny Atlantic coastline has less rain than inland areas. Whichever part of the country you're in, you'll find that both temperatures and humidity levels are high and sunshine is a scarce commodity. Southern districts are the sunniest. 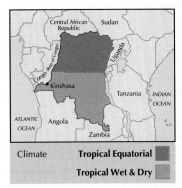 Light clothing is appropriate all year supplemented by rainwear during the wet seasons.

Kinshasa
Alt: 310m (1,000ft)

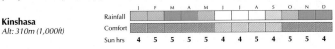

	J	F	M	A	M	J	J	A	S	O	N	D
Rainfall												
Comfort												
Sun hrs	4	5	5	5	5	4	4	5	4	5	5	4

Climate   **Tropical Equatorial**

Tropical Wet & Dry

Zambia

Capital City: **Lusaka** World Map ref: **F5** (In southern hemisphere)

Zambia combines the heat of the tropics with a high plateau topography and this altitude keeps temperatures moderate and makes the country's extensive highlands a pleasant place to be. The north, which is closer to the equator, experiences the most rain with a longer wet season than in the south. The rainy season (November to March) is the hottest period of the year and is usually preceded by a period of very warm, dry weather in September and October. Cooler but dry conditions prevail between May and August. The lowland areas of the Zambesi and its tributary, the Luangwa, are the driest but can be hot, humid and oppressive in the rainy season.  Take light clothes with some warmer options for chilly highland nights.

Lusaka
Alt: 1,280m (4,200ft)

	J	F	M	A	M	J	J	A	S	O	N	D
Rainfall												
Comfort												
Sun hrs	5	5	7	9	9	9	9	9	10	9	7	6

Climate   **Tropical Wet & Dry**

Steppe

Zimbabwe

Capital City: **Harare** World Map ref: **F5** (In southern hemisphere)

Most of Zimbabwe consists of a plateau with an average height of 1,200m (4,000ft). To the north and south are the valleys of the Zambesi and Limpopo, respectively, where altitude falls to 450m (1,500ft).
The upland regions have a healthy and exceptionally pleasant climate with most of the rainfall in the months of November to March and 7 to 9 hours of sunshine daily throughout the year. The eastern highlands have the heaviest rainfall. The lowlands are particularly dry and hot in September/October and generally hot, humid and uncomfortable during the rainy season (from November to March). 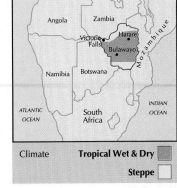 Light clothing should be supplemented in the winter months (our summer) by warmer attire for the evenings, especially if visiting the eastern highlands. A windcheater is recommended if you're planning an early morning game drive.

Harare
Alt: 1,480m (4,900ft)

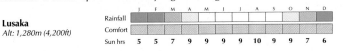

	J	F	M	A	M	J	J	A	S	O	N	D
Rainfall												
Comfort												
Sun hrs	6	7	7	9	9	9	9	10	10	10	7	7

Climate   **Tropical Wet & Dry**

Steppe

Cold but tolerable	Hot but tolerable	Danger of Heatstroke	Key to Comfort
Extremely Cold	Comfortable, Temperate	Hot & Sticky, Very Hot	

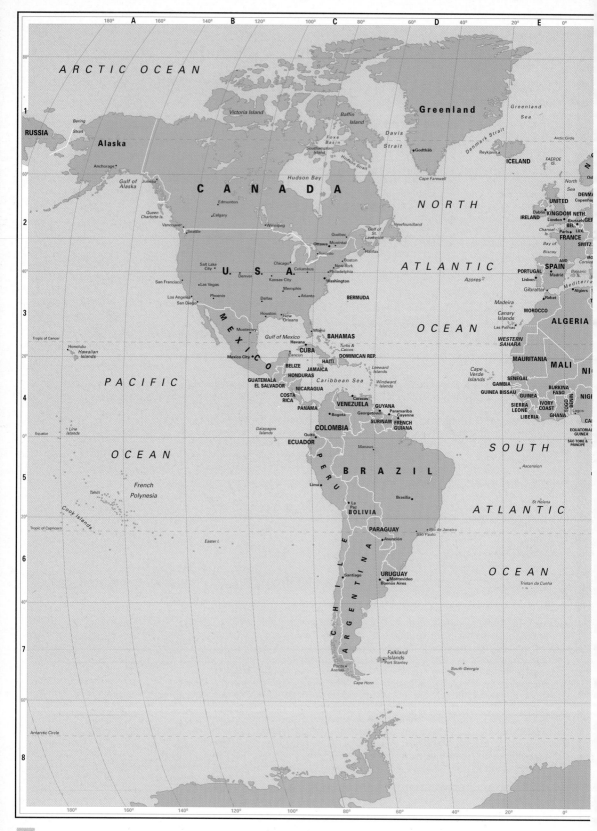

ARCTIC OCEAN

RUSSIA

Alaska

Bering Strait

Anchorage

Juneau

Gulf of Alaska

Queen Charlotte Is.

Vancouver

Seattle

Victoria Island

Baffin Island

Foxe Basin

Southampton Island

Hudson Strait

Hudson Bay

C A N A D A

Edmonton

Calgary

Winnipeg

Quebec

Ottawa

Montreal

Toronto

Gulf of St. Lawrence

Newfoundland

Halifax

Greenland

Greenland Sea

Davis Strait

Godthåb

Denmark Strait

Cape Farewell

Arctic Circle

Reykjavik

ICELAND

FAEROE IS.

North Sea

Oslo

DENMARK

Copenhagen

UNITED KINGDOM

NETH.

GER.

BEL.

LUX.

Dublin

IRELAND

London

Brussels

Channel Is.

Paris

FRANCE

SWITZ.

Bay of Biscay

MO...

Corsica

N O R T H

A T L A N T I C

O C E A N

Azores

PORTUGAL

Lisbon

Gibraltar

SPAIN

Madrid

Balearic Is.

Mediterranean

Rabat

Algiers

Madeira

Canary Islands

Las Palmas

MOROCCO

ALGERIA

WESTERN SAHARA

MAURITANIA

MALI

NI...

Cape Verde Islands

SENEGAL

GAMBIA

GUINEA BISSAU

GUINEA

SIERRA LEONE

LIBERIA

BURKINA FASO

IVORY COAST

GHANA

TOGO

BENIN

NIG...

Lagos

CA...

Salt Lake City

San Francisco

U.S.A.

Denver

Chicago

Columbus

Kansas City

Las Vegas

Los Angeles

San Diego

Phoenix

Dallas

Memphis

Atlanta

Houston

New Orleans

New York

Philadelphia

Washington

Boston

BERMUDA

Tropic of Cancer

Honolulu

Hawaiian Islands

M E X I C O

Monterrey

Gulf of Mexico

Havana

Mexico City

Miami

BAHAMAS

Turks & Caicos

CUBA

Cancun

HAITI

DOMINICAN REP.

BELIZE

JAMAICA

GUATEMALA

HONDURAS

EL SALVADOR

NICARAGUA

COSTA RICA

PANAMA

Caribbean Sea

Leeward Islands

Windward Islands

P A C I F I C

Cape Verde Islands

EQUATORIAL GUINEA

SÃO TOMÉ & PRÍNCIPE

Equator

Line Islands

Galapagos Islands

VENEZUELA

Caracas

Bogota

GUYANA

Georgetown

SURINAM

Paramaribo

FRENCH GUIANA

Cayenne

COLOMBIA

Quito

ECUADOR

Manaus

P E R U

B R A Z I L

Lima

Brasília

S O U T H

Ascension

O C E A N

French Polynesia

Tahiti

Cook Islands

Easter I.

La Paz

BOLIVIA

PARAGUAY

Asunción

Rio de Janeiro

São Paulo

A T L A N T I C

St Helena

Tropic of Capricorn

Santiago

C H I L E

A R G E N T I N A

URUGUAY

Montevideo

Buenos Aires

O C E A N

Tristan da Cunha

Antarctic Circle

Punta Arenas

Falkland Islands

Port Stanley

South Georgia

Cape Horn

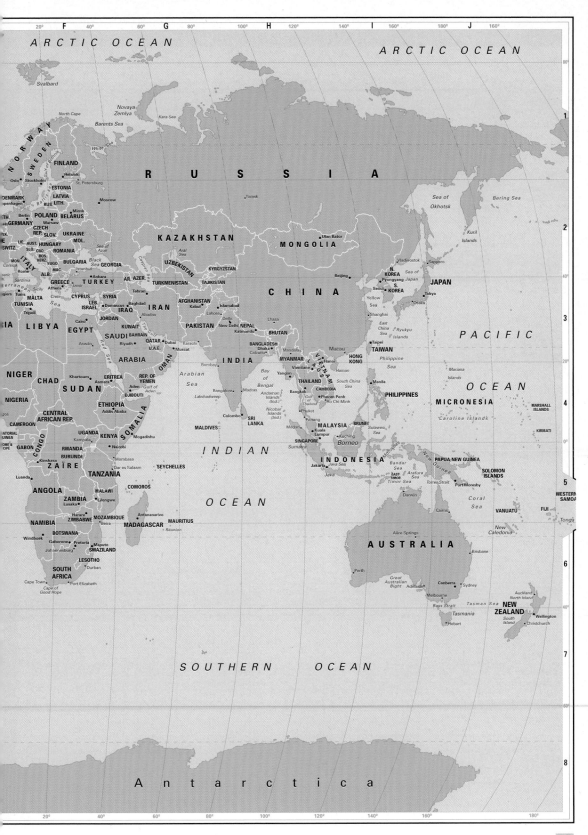

Country	Location	Jan Rain mm	Jan Sun hrs	Jan Temp max	Jan Temp min	Jan Hum %	Feb Rain mm	Feb Sun hrs	Feb Temp max	Feb Temp min	Feb Hum %	Mar Rain mm	Mar Sun hrs	Mar Temp max	Mar Temp min	Mar Hum %	Apr Rain mm	Apr Sun hrs	Apr Temp max	Apr Temp min	Apr Hum %	May Rain mm	May Sun hrs	May Temp max	May Temp min	May Hum %	Jun Rain mm	Jun Sun hrs	Jun Temp max	Jun Temp min	Jun Hum %
Afghanistan	Kabul	31	6	-2	-8	70	36	6	4	-6	62	94	6	12	1	44	102	7	19	6	35	20	10	26	11	32	5	12	31	13	24
Albania	Tirana	135	4	12	2	58	152	4	12	2	54	128	5	15	5	53	117	7	18	8	54	122	8	23	12	56	86	10	28	16	49
Algeria	Algiers	115	5	16	10	63	85	6	17	10	61	59	7	19	12	60	61	7	21	14	61	27	8	24	16	60	13	9	27	19	65
Andorra	Andorra La Vella	34	4	6	-1	*	37	5	7	-1	*	46	6	12	2	*	63	6	14	4	*	105	7	17	6	*	69	7	23	10	*
Angola	Luanda	30	7	30	24	73	36	7	30	24	73	114	7	31	24	73	136	6	30	24	77	16	7	29	23	77	1	7	26	20	75
Anguilla	The Valley	104	8	27	22	69	51	8	27	21	66	58	9	28	22	65	58	9	28	25	67	97	9	29	24	71	91	9	29	24	71
Antigua	St John's	58	8	28	23	69	37	8	28	22	66	49	9	29	23	65	64	9	29	24	67	110	9	30	25	71	51	9	30	25	71
Argentina	Buenos Aires	79	9	29	17	61	71	9	28	17	63	109	7	26	16	69	89	7	22	12	71	76	6	18	8	74	61	4	14	5	78
Armenia	Yerevan	23	3	-2	-9	69	25	4	1	-8	64	28	6	10	-1	56	48	7	19	6	46	53	9	24	10	52	23	11	31	14	39
Australia	Adelaide	20	10	30	16	31	18	9	30	17	32	25	8	27	15	36	46	6	23	13	45	69	5	19	10	56	76	4	16	8	65
	Alice Springs	43	10	36	21	23	33	11	35	21	24	28	10	32	17	25	10	10	27	12	28	15	8	23	8	32	13	9	19	5	35
	Brisbane	163	8	29	21	59	160	7	29	20	60	145	7	28	19	60	94	7	26	16	56	71	7	23	13	55	66	7	21	11	54
	Cairns	422	7	32	23	69	399	7	32	23	68	460	7	31	23	69	287	9	29	21	68	112	7	27	19	68	74	8	26	18	67
	Canberra	48	9	28	13	35	43	8	28	13	39	56	8	24	11	42	41	7	19	7	51	46	6	16	3	57	53	5	12	1	64
	Darwin	386	6	32	25	71	312	6	32	25	72	254	7	33	25	67	97	9	33	24	54	15	9	33	23	47	3	10	31	21	47
	Hobart	48	8	22	12	53	38	7	22	12	56	46	6	20	11	56	48	5	17	9	61	46	4	14	7	63	56	4	12	5	70
	Melbourne	48	8	26	14	48	46	8	26	14	50	56	6	24	13	51	58	5	20	11	56	53	4	17	8	62	53	3	14	7	67
	Perth	8	10	29	17	44	10	10	29	17	43	20	9	27	16	45	43	7	24	14	49	130	6	21	12	58	180	5	18	10	63
	Sydney	89	7	26	18	64	102	7	26	18	65	127	6	24	17	65	135	6	22	14	64	127	6	19	11	63	117	5	16	9	62
Austria	Innsbruck	54	2	1	-7	67	49	4	4	-5	58	41	5	11	0	46	52	5	16	4	43	73	6	20	8	43	110	6	24	11	48
	Vienna	39	2	1	-4	72	44	3	3	-3	66	44	4	8	1	57	45	6	15	6	49	70	7	19	10	52	67	8	23	14	55
Azerbaijan	Baku	13	3	3	0	69	13	3	6	2	66	18	3	11	4	62	23	4	16	9	56	10	7	24	16	48	10	8	29	21	45
Bahamas	Nassau	36	7	25	18	64	38	8	25	18	62	36	9	26	19	64	64	9	27	21	65	117	9	29	22	65	163	8	31	23	68
Bahrain	Manama	8	8	20	14	71	18	9	21	15	70	13	9	24	17	70	8	8	29	21	66	0	10	33	26	63	0	10	36	28	64
Bangladesh	Dhaka	18	9	25	12	46	31	8	28	13	37	58	7	33	16	38	103	6	35	23	42	194	5	34	25	59	321	3	32	26	72
Barbados	Bridgetown	66	9	28	21	71	28	9	28	21	66	33	9	29	21	64	36	9	30	22	65	58	9	31	23	67	112	8	31	23	70
Belarus	Minsk	31	2	-7	-13	81	39	2	-4	-11	76	39	4	1	-7	71	39	5	11	2	62	83	8	18	8	53	63	10	22	11	50
Belgium	Brussels	66	2	4	-1	86	61	3	7	0	81	53	4	10	2	74	60	5	14	5	71	55	6	18	8	65	76	7	22	11	65
	Ostend	41	2	5	1	90	38	3	6	2	86	31	5	9	3	82	38	7	11	6	80	34	7	15	10	78	38	8	18	12	79
Belize	Belize City	137	4	27	19	*	61	5	28	21	*	38	5	29	22	*	56	4	30	23	*	109	3	31	24	*	196	3	31	24	*
Benin	Cotonou	25	7	31	24	66	33	8	32	25	70	93	7	32	26	69	125	7	32	25	70	215	7	31	24	74	385	5	29	23	78
Bermuda	Hamilton	112	5	20	15	70	119	5	20	14	69	122	6	20	15	69	104	8	22	16	70	117	8	24	19	75	112	8	27	22	74
Bhutan	Thimphu	15	6	8	-8	*	48	6	9	-6	*	64	8	12	-3	*	99	6	15	1	*	107	5	17	5	*	119	2	18	9	*
Bolivia	La Paz	114	6	17	6	55	107	5	17	6	55	66	5	18	6	54	33	6	18	4	50	13	8	18	3	34	8	9	17	1	31
Bosnia	Sarajevo	66	2	3	-4	75	64	3	5	-3	67	62	4	10	0	58	64	5	15	5	54	90	6	20	8	55	88	8	24	12	53
Botswana	Francistown	85	7	31	19	41	80	8	31	19	44	50	8	30	17	40	23	9	29	14	39	7	9	26	9	29	3	10	23	6	31
Brazil	Brasilia	317	6	30	17	73	251	6	32	17	69	259	7	32	17	65	117	7	33	17	60	10	9	33	16	51	8	10	32	13	50
	Manaus	249	4	31	24	70	231	4	31	24	71	262	4	31	24	72	221	4	31	24	73	170	5	31	24	72	84	7	31	24	68
	Rio de Janeiro	125	7	29	23	70	122	7	29	23	71	130	7	28	22	74	107	6	27	21	73	79	6	25	18	70	53	6	24	17	69
Brunei	Bandar Seri Begawan	112	7	30	24	81	117	8	30	24	81	150	8	31	24	80	297	9	32	24	78	345	7	32	24	79	351	7	31	24	79
Bulgaria	Sofia	36	2	2	-4	78	28	3	4	-3	69	41	4	10	1	56	61	6	16	5	50	87	7	21	10	52	73	9	24	14	51
Burkina Faso	Ouagadougou	0	9	34	16	14	3	9	37	19	13	7	9	39	23	16	19	8	39	26	28	96	9	37	25	43	119	8	34	24	55
Burundi	Bujumbura	88	5	29	19	*	98	5	29	19	*	111	6	28	19	*	131	5	28	19	*	55	7	29	19	*	7	8	29	18	*
Cambodia	Phnom Penh	7	9	31	21	*	10	9	32	22	*	40	9	34	23	*	77	8	35	24	*	134	7	34	24	*	155	6	33	24	*
Cameroon	Douala	54	5	31	23	68	80	6	32	24	67	208	5	32	23	69	237	5	32	23	69	316	5	31	23	73	495	3	29	23	77
Canada	Calgary	17	3	-4	-16	70	21	4	-3	-15	70	25	5	1	-10	85	35	6	10	-3	51	52	8	16	3	45	88	8	19	7	50
	Halifax	140	3	0	-7	73	119	4	1	-7	68	113	5	4	-4	63	113	6	9	1	62	108	6	14	5	64	94	7	19	10	66
	Montreal	87	3	-6	-13	79	76	4	-4	-11	77	86	5	2	-5	76	83	5	11	2	73	81	7	18	9	71	91	8	23	14	74
	Ottawa	62	3	-7	-16	75	58	4	-5	-15	74	67	5	1	-8	67	69	6	11	0	56	70	7	19	7	53	78	8	24	12	56
	Toronto	66	2	-1	-8	71	58	4	0	-7	67	64	4	4	-3	62	66	6	13	3	55	71	7	18	9	55	62	8	24	14	55
	Vancouver	214	2	6	0	85	161	3	7	1	79	151	4	10	3	73	90	6	14	5	65	69	8	17	8	63	65	7	20	11	63
	Winnipeg	26	4	-13	-22	83	20	5	-10	-21	85	25	5	-3	-13	78	30	7	9	-2	58	50	8	18	5	48	86	8	22	10	54
Cape Verde	Praia	1	7	25	20	55	1	8	26	20	50	1	9	27	20	48	1	10	27	21	52	0	10	28	21	55	1	9	28	22	59
Cayman Islands	Grand Cayman	35	8	27	20	71	22	8	27	20	66	13	9	28	21	64	64	9	29	22	65	232	8	30	22	67	121	8	31	23	70
Central African Rep	Bangui	20	7	32	20	49	39	7	34	21	47	116	6	33	22	57	142	6	32	22	61	167	6	31	22	65	134	6	30	22	68
Chad	Ndjamena	0	11	33	14	14	0	10	36	16	10	1	9	39	21	11	7	9	41	24	16	29	9	40	25	25	66	8	37	24	40
Channel Islands	Jersey - St Helier	89	2	9	5	82	68	3	8	4	77	57	5	11	6	71	43	7	13	7	65	44	8	16	10	66	39	9	19	13	67
Chile	Santiago	3	11	29	12	38	3	9	29	11	40	5	9	27	9	41	13	6	23	7	46	64	4	18	5	58	84	3	14	3	64
China	Beijing	4	7	1	-10	50	5	7	4	-8	50	8	8	11	-1	48	17	8	21	7	46	35	9	27	13	49	78	9	31	18	56
	Guangzhou - Canton	46	4	26	3	51	69	3	27	6	63	91	3	28	9	72	150	3	32	14	68	252	5	33	20	68	269	5	34	22	63
	Lhasa	0	6	7	-10	71	13	6	9	-7	71	8	8	12	-2	72	5	7	16	1	67	25	5	19	5	59	64	2	24	9	64
	Shanghai	48	4	8	1	58	58	4	8	1	60	84	4	13	4	53	94	5	19	10	58	94	5	25	15	56	180	5	28	19	66
Colombia	Bogota	58	6	19	9	51	66	5	20	9	53	102	4	19	10	54	147	3	19	11	57	114	3	19	11	58	61	4	18	11	56 *

Rain mm Average monthly rainfall   **Sun hrs** Average daily hours of sunshine   **Temp °C** Average daily maximum/minimum temperature
Hum % Average midday humidity   ★ Figures not available

Rainfall Conversion Scale	mm	5	25	50	75	100	150	200	300	600	1200
	in	0.2	1	2	3	4	6	8	12	24	48

Weather Statistics

July					August					September					October					November					December					Location	Country
Rain mm	Sun hrs	Temp max	min	Hum %	Rain mm	Sun hrs	Temp max	min	Hum %	Rain mm	Sun hrs	Temp max	min	Hum %	Rain mm	Sun hrs	Temp max	min	Hum %	Rain mm	Sun hrs	Temp max	min	Hum %	Rain mm	Sun hrs	Temp max	min	Hum %		
3	11	33	16	22	3	11	33	15	23	0	10	29	11	18	15	9	23	6	22	20	8	17	1	31	10	6	8	-3	53	Kabul	**Afghanistan**
32	11	31	17	42	32	11	31	17	39	60	9	27	14	45	105	7	23	10	49	211	3	17	8	63	173	2	14	5	63	Tirana	**Albania**
3	10	28	22	64	7	10	30	23	63	22	8	28	21	62	89	6	25	18	61	108	5	21	14	61	140	4	17	11	62	Algiers	**Algeria**
65	9	26	12	*	98	8	24	12	*	81	7	22	10	*	73	5	16	6	*	68	5	10	2	*	69	4	6	-1	*	Andorra La Vella	**Andorra**
1	5	24	18	77	1	5	24	18	77	2	5	25	20	76	7	5	27	22	76	32	6	29	23	76	31	6	29	23	73	Luanda	**Angola**
112	9	30	24	71	132	9	30	24	72	152	8	30	24	73	137	8	29	24	73	183	8	29	23	74	114	8	28	23	72	The Valley	**Anguilla**
88	9	31	25	71	98	9	31	25	72	128	8	31	25	73	139	8	30	25	73	139	8	30	24	74	90	8	29	24	72	St John's	**Antigua**
56	5	14	6	74	61	6	16	6	74	79	6	18	8	68	86	8	21	10	65	84	9	24	13	60	99	9	28	16	62	Buenos Aires	**Argentina**
15	12	34	17	36	8	11	33	18	36	13	10	28	13	39	23	8	21	7	47	31	5	10	1	64	28	3	3	-3	75	Yerevan	**Armenia**
66	4	15	7	63	66	5	17	8	57	53	6	19	9	52	43	7	23	11	42	28	8	26	13	36	25	9	28	15	32	Adelaide	**Australia**
8	9	19	4	31	8	10	23	6	25	8	10	27	9	22	18	10	31	14	21	31	11	34	18	21	38	10	36	20	22	Alice Springs	
56	7	20	9	51	48	8	22	10	49	48	8	24	13	51	64	8	27	16	53	94	8	28	18	57	127	9	29	19	56	Brisbane	
41	9	26	16	63	43	9	27	17	61	43	9	28	18	61	53	9	30	20	63	99	9	31	21	62	221	8	32	23	66	Cairns	
46	5	11	1	63	56	6	13	2	59	41	8	16	3	50	56	7	20	6	45	48	9	24	9	41	51	9	27	12	36	Canberra	
0	10	31	19	44	3	10	32	21	45	13	10	33	23	49	51	10	34	25	52	119	8	34	26	58	239	7	33	26	65	Darwin	
53	4	11	4	69	48	5	13	5	61	53	6	15	6	58	58	7	17	8	55	58	6	19	9	52	57	7	21	11	54	Hobart	
48	4	13	6	65	48	4	15	6	60	58	5	17	8	55	66	6	19	9	52	58	6	22	11	52	58	7	24	12	51	Melbourne	
170	5	17	9	63	145	6	18	9	61	86	7	19	10	58	56	8	21	12	55	20	10	24	14	49	13	10	27	16	47	Perth	
117	6	16	8	60	76	7	17	9	56	74	7	19	11	55	71	8	22	13	57	74	7	23	16	60	74	8	25	17	62	Sydney	
134	7	25	13	52	108	6	24	12	52	81	6	21	10	53	67	5	15	5	55	53	3	8	0	65	46	2	2	-4	70	Innsbruck	**Austria**
84	9	25	15	54	72	8	24	15	54	42	6	20	11	56	56	4	14	7	64	52	2	7	3	74	45	1	3	-1	76	Vienna	
5	8	32	24	42	5	7	32	24	41	5	5	27	19	45	10	4	19	13	51	13	4	12	7	60	13	3	8	3	68	Baku	**Azerbaijan**
147	9	31	24	69	135	9	32	24	70	175	7	31	24	73	165	7	29	23	71	71	7	27	21	68	33	7	26	19	66	Nassau	**Bahamas**
0	10	37	29	67	0	11	38	29	65	0	10	36	27	64	0	10	32	24	66	18	8	28	21	70	18	7	22	16	77	Manama	**Bahrain**
437	2	31	26	74	305	2	31	26	74	254	3	31	26	71	169	6	31	24	65	28	8	29	18	53	2	6	26	13	50	Dhaka	**Bangladesh**
147	9	30	23	71	147	9	31	23	72	170	8	31	23	73	178	8	30	23	76	206	8	29	23	78	97	8	28	22	73	Bridgetown	**Barbados**
63	9	23	12	52	82	8	22	12	56	45	6	17	8	55	44	3	11	4	76	66	1	3	-1	87	42	1	-3	-8	87	Minsk	**Belarus**
95	6	23	12	68	80	6	22	12	70	63	5	21	11	69	83	4	15	7	77	75	2	9	3	85	88	1	6	0	86	Brussels	**Belgium**
62	7	20	13	80	58	7	20	13	80	56	6	19	12	80	68	4	15	9	83	74	2	10	5	89	60	1	6	2	91	Ostend	
163	3	31	24	*	170	3	31	24	*	244	3	31	23	*	305	3	30	22	*	226	3	28	20	*	185	3	27	20	*	Belize City	**Belize**
153	4	28	23	77	41	5	28	23	76	85	5	29	24	76	167	6	30	23	75	55	8	31	24	74	18	7	31	24	71	Cotonou	**Benin**
114	10	29	24	73	137	9	30	24	69	132	8	29	23	73	147	6	26	21	72	127	6	23	19	70	119	5	21	16	70	Hamilton	**Bermuda**
130	2	19	11	*	117	3	19	10	*	102	5	18	8	*	53	10	16	2	*	18	10	12	-3	*	5	9	9	-7	*	Thimphu	**Bhutan**
10	9	17	1	34	13	8	17	2	31	28	7	18	3	38	41	6	19	4	41	48	6	19	6	42	94	6	18	6	41	La Paz	**Bolivia**
71	9	26	13	49	70	9	27	13	45	78	7	23	10	52	103	6	16	6	62	91	2	10	3	71	85	2	6	-1	75	Sarajevo	**Bosnia**
1	9	24	6	29	1	10	26	8	25	3	10	30	13	25	23	9	32	16	29	51	8	32	18	37	88	8	31	19	44	Francistown	**Botswana**
0	10	32	13	48	8	10	34	15	40	58	8	34	18	42	135	7	34	17	51	239	5	32	17	65	241	5	31	17	73	Brasilia	**Brazil**
58	8	32	24	64	38	8	33	24	59	46	8	33	24	57	107	7	33	24	59	142	6	33	24	63	203	5	32	24	68	Manaus	
41	6	24	18	68	43	7	24	18	66	66	5	24	19	72	79	5	25	19	72	104	6	26	20	72	137	6	28	22	72	Rio de Janeiro	
318	7	31	25	78	297	7	31	24	76	417	6	31	24	77	465	7	31	24	78	419	7	31	24	78	285	7	30	24	79	Bandar Seri Begawan	**Brunei**
68	10	27	16	46	64	10	26	15	46	41	7	22	11	51	65	5	17	8	59	48	3	9	3	72	49	1	4	-2	77	Sofia	**Bulgaria**
181	7	32	22	64	255	6	30	22	70	166	7	32	22	65	40	9	35	23	46	2	9	36	20	23	1	8	34	17	16	Ouagadougou	**Burkina Faso**
3	9	29	17	*	13	8	30	18	*	32	7	31	19	*	67	6	30	20	*	90	5	28	19	*	112	5	28	19	*	Bujumbura	**Burundi**
171	6	32	24	*	160	6	32	25	*	224	5	31	25	*	257	7	30	24	*	127	8	30	23	*	45	9	30	22	*	Phnom Penh	**Cambodia**
635	2	27	23	83	774	1	27	22	84	645	2	28	23	80	391	4	30	22	83	147	5	31	23	72	48	5	31	23	69	Douala	**Cameroon**
58	10	24	10	48	59	9	22	8	47	35	6	17	4	49	23	5	12	-1	55	16	4	3	-8	65	15	3	-1	-12	69	Calgary	**Canada**
94	8	23	14	66	95	7	23	14	66	117	6	20	12	64	120	5	14	7	66	143	3	9	2	72	132	3	3	-4	73	Halifax	
98	8	26	17	76	87	6	25	16	79	96	6	20	11	83	84	4	14	6	81	89	2	6	0	81	89	2	-3	-9	79	Montreal	
82	9	27	14	53	83	8	26	14	54	82	6	20	9	59	67	4	13	4	62	69	3	5	-2	70	78	2	-4	-12	74	Ottawa	
74	9	27	17	54	61	8	26	16	56	66	7	22	12	59	58	5	14	7	58	63	3	7	2	67	61	2	1	-4	71	Toronto	
39	9	23	13	62	44	8	22	12	65	83	6	19	10	72	172	4	14	7	80	198	3	9	3	85	243	2	7	2	88	Vancouver	
73	10	26	14	55	72	9	25	13	55	52	6	19	7	61	38	5	12	1	66	28	3	-1	-9	81	22	3	-9	-17	85	Winnipeg	
11	7	28	23	65	57	6	29	24	67	91	7	29	24	69	28	8	30	24	63	12	8	28	23	59	2	7	26	21	57	Praia	**Cape Verde**
108	9	32	24	71	146	8	32	24	72	166	7	31	23	73	208	7	30	23	76	112	8	29	22	78	77	7	28	21	73	Grand Cayman	**Cayman Islands**
174	4	29	21	72	240	4	29	21	70	185	5	30	21	68	190	5	30	21	68	89	6	31	21	65	24	7	32	19	52	Bangui	**Central African Rep**
150	7	33	23	57	247	6	31	22	68	102	7	33	22	59	22	9	36	21	33	1	10	36	18	18	1	11	34	15	14	Ndjamena	**Chad**
48	8	21	15	64	67	8	21	16	64	58	6	20	14	68	74	5	16	11	72	101	3	12	8	80	99	2	10	6	80	St Helier - Jersey	**Channel Islands**
76	3	15	3	60	56	4	17	4	56	31	5	19	6	55	15	6	22	7	50	8	9	26	9	41	5	10	28	11	38	Santiago	**Chile**
243	7	31	21	72	141	7	30	20	74	58	8	26	14	67	16	8	20	6	59	11	6	9	-2	56	3	6	3	-8	51	Beijing	**China**
252	7	36	24	62	244	7	36	23	63	137	7	34	21	55	58	7	32	16	50	41	6	29	9	46	36	5	27	5	51	Canton - Guangzhou	
122	2	23	9	71	89	3	22	9	72	66	5	21	7	71	13	10	17	1	64	3	10	13	-5	71	0	9	9	-9	71	Lhasa	
147	7	32	23	66	142	7	32	23	65	130	5	28	19	64	71	6	23	14	53	51	5	17	7	55	36	5	12	2	62	Shanghai	
51	4	18	10	56	56	4	18	10	54	61	4	19	9	54	160	3	19	10	64	119	4	19	10	64	66	5	19	9	56	Bogota	**Colombia**

Rain mm Average monthly rainfall **Sun hrs** Average daily hours of sunshine **Temp °C** Average daily maximum/minimum temperature
Hum % Average midday humidity ⋆ Figures not available

°C	-40	-30	-20	-10	0	10	20	30	40	°C
°F	-40	-30	-20	-10	0	10	20 30 40	50 60 70	80 90 100	110	°F

Temperature Conversion Scale

Weather Statistics

Country	Location	Jan Rain mm	Jan Sun hrs	Jan Temp max	Jan Temp min	Jan Hum %	Feb Rain mm	Feb Sun hrs	Feb Temp max	Feb Temp min	Feb Hum %	Mar Rain mm	Mar Sun hrs	Mar Temp max	Mar Temp min	Mar Hum %	Apr Rain mm	Apr Sun hrs	Apr Temp max	Apr Temp min	Apr Hum %	May Rain mm	May Sun hrs	May Temp max	May Temp min	May Hum %	Jun Rain mm	Jun Sun hrs	Jun Temp max	Jun Temp min	Jun Hum %
Comoros	Moroni	345	6	30	24	78	311	6	30	24	77	300	7	31	23	75	296	6	30	23	74	233	7	29	22	75	215	8	28	20	76
Congo	Brazzaville	139	5	30	21	69	131	5	31	21	65	195	5	31	21	64	211	6	32	22	66	127	5	30	21	67	4	5	28	19	67
Cook Islands	Rarotonga	234	6	29	23	75	257	6	29	23	79	284	6	28	23	78	196	6	27	22	77	150	5	26	21	76	122	5	25	19	75
Costa Rica	San José	15	7	24	14	63	5	8	24	14	57	20	8	26	15	55	46	7	26	17	60	229	5	27	17	70	241	4	26	17	74
Croatia	Dubrovnik	139	4	12	6	59	125	5	13	6	63	104	5	14	8	63	104	6	17	11	66	75	8	21	14	69	48	10	25	18	66
	Zagreb	55	2	3	-2	75	54	4	6	-1	65	47	5	11	3	57	60	6	17	8	51	85	7	21	12	55	95	8	25	15	55
Cuba	Havana	71	6	26	18	64	46	6	26	18	51	46	7	27	19	58	58	7	29	21	58	119	8	30	22	62	165	6	31	23	65
Cyprus	Nicosia	76	5	15	5	66	45	7	16	5	61	36	7	19	7	55	18	9	24	10	46	22	11	29	14	41	9	13	34	18	37
Czech Republic	Prague	18	2	0	-5	73	18	3	1	-4	67	18	5	7	-1	55	27	6	12	3	47	48	8	18	8	45	54	9	21	11	46
Denmark	Copenhagen	49	1	2	-2	85	39	2	2	-3	83	32	4	5	-1	78	38	5	10	3	68	43	8	16	8	59	47	8	19	11	60
Djibouti	Djibouti	16	8	29	22	65	10	8	29	23	65	17	9	30	24	65	14	9	32	26	67	6	10	34	27	61	1	8	38	30	48
Dominica	Roseau	132	8	29	20	65	74	8	29	19	62	74	9	31	20	59	81	8	31	21	61	97	8	32	22	61	196	7	32	23	65
Dominican Rep	Santo Domingo	61	6	29	19	64	36	6	29	19	58	48	7	29	19	60	99	7	29	21	62	173	6	30	22	65	158	6	31	22	66
Ecuador	Galapagos Islands	20	6	30	22	*	36	8	30	24	*	28	8	31	24	*	18	8	31	24	*	0	8	30	23	*	0	8	28	22	*
	Quito	99	5	22	8	54	112	5	22	8	59	142	4	22	8	59	175	5	21	8	60	137	5	21	8	60	43	6	22	7	51
Egypt	Cairo	4	7	19	9	43	4	8	21	9	39	3	9	24	12	33	1	10	28	14	28	2	10	32	18	25	1	12	35	20	27
	Luxor	1	10	23	6	38	1	11	25	7	32	1	10	29	11	23	1	11	35	16	18	1	11	39	20	15	0	12	41	23	15
El Salvador	San Salvador	8	10	32	16	45	5	10	33	16	43	10	10	34	17	44	43	8	34	18	50	196	8	33	19	60	328	6	31	19	66
Equatorial Guinea	Malabo	39	4	30	20	79	34	5	31	21	78	118	3	31	21	79	186	4	31	21	82	179	4	30	22	83	223	3	29	21	85
Eritrea	Asmara	1	9	23	6	35	1	9	24	7	31	11	9	25	9	28	27	9	25	10	31	43	10	25	11	31	37	7	26	11	31
Estonia	Tallinn	39	1	-4	-10	86	30	2	-4	-11	83	21	4	0	-7	77	31	6	7	0	66	44	7	14	5	63	40	11	19	10	55
Ethiopia	Addis Ababa	13	9	23	6	38	35	9	24	7	47	67	8	25	9	45	91	7	24	10	47	81	8	25	9	39	117	6	23	10	52
Falkland Islands	Stanley	71	7	13	6	*	58	6	13	5	*	64	5	12	4	*	66	3	9	3	*	66	2	7	1	*	53	2	5	-1	*
Fiji	Suva	290	7	29	23	74	272	6	29	23	76	368	6	29	23	76	310	7	29	23	77	257	7	28	22	79	170	7	27	21	74
Finland	Helsinki	56	1	-3	-9	87	42	3	-4	-9	82	36	4	0	-7	70	44	6	6	-1	66	41	9	14	4	58	51	10	19	9	59
France	Bordeaux	90	3	9	2	80	75	4	11	2	73	63	5	15	4	64	48	7	17	6	60	61	7	20	9	60	65	8	24	12	62
	Cherbourg	109	2	8	4	79	75	2	8	4	76	62	5	10	5	74	49	5	12	7	73	41	7	15	9	73	39	7	18	12	74
	Lyon	52	2	5	-1	80	46	3	7	0	72	53	5	13	3	60	56	6	16	6	56	69	8	20	9	56	85	8	24	13	55
	Nice	68	5	13	4	62	61	6	13	5	62	73	6	15	7	67	73	8	17	9	69	68	9	20	13	70	35	10	24	16	71
	Paris	56	2	6	1	80	46	3	7	1	73	35	5	12	4	63	42	6	16	6	54	57	7	20	10	55	54	8	23	13	58
	Corsica - Ajaccio	76	4	13	3	66	65	5	14	4	67	53	6	16	5	67	48	8	18	7	66	50	10	21	10	69	21	11	25	14	65
French Guiana	Cayenne	366	5	29	23	80	312	4	29	23	80	401	4	29	23	80	480	4	30	24	81	551	4	29	23	83	394	6	31	23	79
French Polynesia	Tahiti	252	5	32	22	77	244	6	32	22	77	429	7	32	22	78	142	7	32	22	78	102	7	31	21	78	76	7	30	21	79
Gabon	Libreville	298	5	29	24	79	270	6	30	24	78	418	5	30	24	78	360	5	30	24	78	276	5	29	24	78	18	4	28	23	74
Gambia	Banjul	1	9	30	19	40	2	10	31	19	45	0	10	32	20	47	0	10	30	20	55	5	10	30	22	62	86	9	31	24	67
Georgia	Tbilisi	17	3	7	-1	60	15	4	9	0	53	27	5	13	3	50	61	5	17	8	49	75	7	24	12	47	54	9	28	16	42
Germany	Berlin	46	2	2	-3	82	40	2	3	-3	78	33	5	8	0	67	42	6	13	4	60	49	8	19	8	57	65	8	22	12	58
	Frankfurt	58	1	3	-2	77	44	2	5	-1	70	38	4	11	2	57	44	5	16	6	51	55	7	20	9	50	73	8	23	13	52
	Hamburg	58	2	2	-2	84	48	2	3	-2	80	39	4	7	-1	68	52	6	13	3	61	56	7	18	7	57	63	8	21	11	59
	Munich	59	2	1	-5	77	53	3	3	-5	71	48	5	9	-1	61	62	6	14	3	55	109	7	18	7	57	125	8	21	11	58
Ghana	Accra	20	7	32	23	64	29	8	32	24	65	70	7	32	24	67	90	7	32	24	68	146	7	31	23	72	235	5	29	23	78
Gibraltar	Gibraltar	152	6	16	10	70	98	7	17	11	67	106	7	18	12	66	59	8	20	13	64	25	10	23	15	62	4	11	25	18	62
Greece	Athens	62	4	13	6	62	37	5	14	7	57	37	6	16	8	54	23	8	20	11	48	23	9	25	16	47	14	11	30	20	39
	Corfu - Corfu Town	196	4	14	6	66	132	5	15	6	64	100	6	16	8	63	70	8	19	10	63	41	10	23	13	60	14	11	28	17	54
	Crete - Heraklion	95	3	16	9	63	69	5	16	9	59	42	6	17	9	59	13	10	23	15	62	13	12	27	19	58	3	12	27	19	58
Greenland	Godthåb	27	1	-5	-12	90	23	4	-4	-11	92	17	6	-3	-10	93	25	6	0	-7	93	30	6	5	-2	94	49	5	10	2	93
Grenada	St George's	140	9	29	17	70	100	8	29	17	68	110	7	31	18	65	95	8	32	19	64	160	8	33	20	65	230	7	33	21	69
Guadeloupe	Camp Jacob	234	7	25	18	80	155	8	24	17	77	206	8	25	17	75	185	8	26	18	76	292	7	27	19	77	358	8	27	21	76
Guatemala	Guatemala City	2	9	23	12	65	3	5	25	12	62	13	5	27	14	51	31	4	28	14	51	152	3	29	16	55	274	1	27	16	70
Guinea	Conakry	1	5	31	22	59	1	7	31	22	58	11	9	32	23	58	27	8	32	24	59	145	5	31	24	67	468	3	29	23	78
Guinea-Bissau	Bissau	1	8	32	18	34	1	9	33	19	36	1	10	34	20	42	1	10	33	21	46	24	9	33	22	55	167	7	31	23	66
Guyana	Georgetown	203	6	29	23	75	114	7	29	23	72	175	7	29	24	71	140	7	29	24	71	290	6	29	24	75	302	6	29	24	77
Haiti	Port-au-Prince	33	9	31	20	64	58	9	31	20	64	86	9	32	21	65	160	9	32	22	65	231	8	32	22	54	102	8	33	23	50
Honduras	Tegucigalpa	12	9	25	14	*	2	9	27	14	*	1	9	29	15	*	30	8	30	17	*	180	8	30	18	*	177	6	28	18	*
Hong Kong	Hong Kong	33	5	18	13	66	46	4	17	13	73	74	3	19	16	74	137	4	24	19	77	292	5	28	23	78	394	5	29	26	77
Hungary	Budapest	37	2	1	-4	76	44	3	4	-2	68	38	5	10	2	55	45	7	17	7	48	72	8	22	11	49	69	9	26	15	49
Iceland	Reykjavik	89	1	2	-2	79	64	2	3	-2	75	62	4	4	-1	72	56	5	6	1	73	42	6	10	4	67	42	6	12	7	72
India	Bombay	3	9	28	19	61	3	10	28	19	62	3	9	30	22	65	0	10	32	24	67	18	10	33	27	68	485	5	32	26	77
	Calcutta	10	8	27	13	52	31	9	29	15	45	36	9	34	21	46	43	9	36	24	56	140	8	36	25	62	297	5	33	26	75
	Delhi	23	7	21	7	41	18	8	24	9	35	13	8	31	14	23	8	9	36	20	19	13	8	41	26	20	74	6	39	28	36
	Goa	1	9	29	21	61	1	9	29	21	61	1	9	31	24	68	18	10	32	26	70	66	10	32	27	73	752	5	31	25	85
	Madras	36	9	29	19	67	10	10	31	20	66	8	10	33	22	67	15	10	35	26	67	25	9	38	28	67	48	7	38	27	61
	Srinagar	74	3	5	-2	76	71	4	7	-1	68	91	4	14	3	57	94	6	19	7	52	61	8	24	11	43	36	8	29	14	40

Rain mm Average monthly rainfall   **Sun hrs** Average daily hours of sunshine   **Temp °C** Average daily maximum/minimum temperature   **Hum %** Average midday humidity   ★ Figures not available

Rainfall Conversion Scale

mm	5	25	50	75	100	150	200	300	600	1200
in	0.2	1	2	3	4	6	8	12	24	48

Rain mm	Sun hrs	Temp °C max	min	Hum %	Rain mm	Sun hrs	Temp °C max	min	Hum %	Rain mm	Sun hrs	Temp °C max	min	Hum %	Rain mm	Sun hrs	Temp °C max	min	Hum %	Rain mm	Sun hrs	Temp °C max	min	Hum %	Rain mm	Sun hrs	Temp °C max	min	Hum %	Location	Country
July					**August**					**September**					**October**					**November**					**December**						
194	8	28	19	76	118	7	27	19	75	117	7	28	19	75	91	8	29	21	75	102	8	31	22	74	220	7	31	23	77	Moroni	**Comoros**
1	4	27	17	65	2	5	28	18	60	37	4	30	20	60	135	5	30	21	64	235	5	30	21	68	179	5	30	21	70	Brazzaville	**Congo**
112	6	25	18	70	119	6	25	18	71	127	6	25	19	68	135	6	26	20	71	163	6	27	21	72	206	6	28	22	72	Rarotonga	**Cook Islands**
211	4	25	17	74	241	4	26	16	73	305	5	26	16	76	300	4	25	16	78	145	5	25	16	71	41	6	24	14	67	San José	**Costa Rica**
26	12	29	21	61	38	11	28	21	61	101	9	25	18	63	162	7	21	14	63	198	4	17	10	65	178	3	14	8	65	Dubrovnik	**Croatia**
79	9	27	17	52	74	9	27	16	53	71	7	22	13	57	88	4	15	8	67	88	2	9	4	76	69	2	5	0	79	Zagreb	
125	6	32	24	62	135	6	32	24	64	150	5	31	24	66	173	5	29	23	68	79	5	27	21	65	58	5	26	19	64	Havana	**Cuba**
1	13	37	21	34	2	12	37	21	35	10	11	33	18	38	25	9	28	14	45	33	7	22	10	53	68	5	17	7	63	Nicosia	**Cyprus**
68	8	23	13	49	55	8	22	13	48	31	6	18	9	51	33	4	12	5	60	20	2	5	1	73	21	1	1	-3	78	Prague	**Czech Republic**
71	8	22	14	62	66	7	21	14	64	62	5	18	11	69	59	3	12	7	76	48	1	7	3	83	49	1	4	1	87	Copenhagen	**Denmark**
11	8	42	31	32	14	9	41	30	35	4	9	38	29	48	9	10	33	26	59	35	10	31	24	61	10	8	29	22	62	Djibouti	**Djibouti**
274	8	32	22	69	262	8	32	23	69	226	8	32	23	67	198	7	32	22	70	224	8	31	22	70	163	8	30	21	67	Roseau	**Dominica**
163	6	31	22	66	160	7	31	23	66	185	7	31	22	66	152	6	31	22	66	122	6	30	21	66	61	6	29	19	66	Santo Domingo	**Dominican Rep**
0	6	27	21	*	0	6	27	19	*	0	5	27	19	*	0	5	27	19	*	0	6	27	20	*	0	6	28	21	*	Galapagos Islands	**Ecuador**
20	7	22	7	43	31	7	23	7	40	69	8	23	7	44	112	5	22	8	53	97	6	22	7	53	79	6	22	8	54	Quito	
0	12	35	22	31	0	11	35	22	35	1	10	33	20	37	1	9	30	18	36	3	8	26	14	42	7	6	21	10	46	Cairo	**Egypt**
0	12	41	23	17	1	11	41	24	17	1	11	39	22	21	1	11	35	18	28	1	10	30	12	32	0	10	25	7	39	Luxor	
292	8	32	19	62	297	8	32	19	62	307	6	31	19	69	150	7	31	18	66	41	9	31	17	56	10	10	32	16	50	San Salvador	**El Salvador**
263	2	27	21	87	181	2	28	21	88	262	2	28	21	87	231	2	28	21	87	92	3	29	21	86	30	4	30	21	83	Malabo	**Equatorial Guinea**
158	5	20	12	64	138	6	20	12	64	24	9	25	10	36	10	9	22	9	48	15	9	23	9	41	4	9	22	7	34	Asmara	**Eritrea**
68	10	20	12	59	78	9	19	11	64	71	5	15	9	69	68	2	10	4	79	56	1	3	-1	86	39	0	-1	-7	87	Tallinn	**Estonia**
247	3	20	11	65	255	3	20	11	67	167	5	21	10	58	29	8	22	7	40	8	9	23	5	40	5	9	22	5	33	Addis Ababa	**Ethiopia**
51	2	4	-1	*	51	3	5	-1	*	38	4	7	1	*	41	5	9	2	*	51	7	11	3	*	71	7	12	4	*	Stanley	**Falkland Islands**
125	7	26	20	73	211	8	26	20	74	196	7	27	21	73	211	7	27	21	73	249	7	28	22	74	318	7	29	23	74	Suva	**Fiji**
68	9	22	13	63	72	8	20	12	67	71	5	15	8	72	73	3	8	3	79	68	1	3	-1	86	66	1	-1	-5	•89	Helsinki	**Finland**
56	9	25	14	61	70	8	26	14	60	84	7	23	12	67	83	5	18	8	71	96	3	13	5	80	109	2	9	3	83	Bordeaux	**France**
55	8	19	14	74	71	7	20	14	75	79	5	19	13	74	99	2	15	10	73	133	2	12	8	77	119	2	10	5	79	Cherbourg	
56	9	27	15	50	89	8	26	14	54	93	7	23	12	60	77	4	16	7	69	80	2	10	4	78	57	2	6	0	80	Lyon	
20	11	27	18	69	27	10	27	18	70	77	8	25	16	67	124	7	21	12	65	129	5	17	8	64	107	5	13	5	62	Nice	
59	8	25	15	57	64	7	24	14	61	55	6	21	12	65	50	4	16	8	71	51	2	10	5	79	50	2	7	2	82	Paris	
10	12	27	16	65	16	11	28	16	64	50	9	26	15	64	88	7	22	11	63	97	5	18	7	66	98	4	15	4	66	Ajaccio - Corsica	
175	7	31	23	75	71	8	32	23	71	31	9	33	23	69	33	9	33	23	69	117	8	32	23	74	272	6	30	23	79	Cayenne	**French Guiana**
53	7	30	20	77	43	7	30	20	78	53	8	30	21	76	89	7	31	21	76	150	7	31	22	77	249	6	31	22	78	Tahiti	**French Polynesia**
1	4	26	22	73	3	7	27	22	74	94	3	28	23	77	388	4	28	24	81	527	4	28	23	82	347	5	29	24	80	Libreville	**Gabon**
255	6	31	25	72	458	6	30	24	76	286	6	31	24	73	82	8	32	25	65	27	8	32	23	62	2	9	30	20	48	Banjul	**Gambia**
46	9	31	19	40	46	8	30	19	42	45	7	26	15	49	30	6	20	10	53	27	3	14	5	60	19	3	9	1	65	Tbilisi	**Georgia**
73	8	24	14	61	69	7	23	13	61	48	6	20	10	65	49	4	13	6	73	46	2	7	2	83	43	1	3	-1	86	Berlin	**Germany**
70	7	25	15	53	76	7	24	14	54	57	5	21	11	60	52	3	14	7	68	55	1	8	3	77	54	1	4	0	81	Frankfurt	
83	7	22	13	61	81	7	22	12	63	62	6	19	10	65	59	3	13	6	74	57	1	7	3	83	57	1	4	0	86	Hamburg	
139	8	23	13	57	107	8	23	12	58	85	6	20	9	61	66	4	13	4	68	57	2	7	0	78	47	2	2	-4	82	Munich	
70	5	27	22	76	21	5	27	21	75	54	6	29	22	73	77	7	30	22	72	35	8	31	23	70	18	8	31	23	66	Accra	**Ghana**
1	11	28	20	60	3	11	29	21	60	23	9	26	19	65	55	7	23	17	69	114	6	19	14	72	127	6	17	11	70	Gibraltar	**Gibraltar**
6	12	33	23	34	7	12	33	23	34	15	9	29	19	42	51	7	24	15	52	56	5	19	12	61	71	4	15	8	63	Athens	**Greece**
4	11	31	19	50	20	11	32	19	48	95	9	28	17	58	184	7	23	14	62	237	4	19	11	66	259	3	16	8	68	Corfu Town - Corfu	
1	13	29	22	57	1	12	29	22	60	11	10	27	19	61	64	6	24	17	63	71	6	21	14	65	79	4	18	11	65	Heraklion - Crete	
58	6	12	3	96	70	4	11	3	97	80	3	7	1	96	75	2	2	-4	96	47	1	-1	-7	93	25	0	-4	-10	89	Godthåb	**Greenland**
245	8	33	22	71	280	8	33	22	69	260	8	32	22	70	245	8	31	21	69	240	8	31	20	75	210	8	30	18	71	St George's	**Grenada**
447	7	27	20	76	389	7	28	21	75	417	7	28	21	78	315	7	27	20	81	312	7	27	19	79	257	7	26	18	81	Camp Jacob	**Guadeloupe**
203	2	26	16	67	198	1	26	16	72	231	2	26	16	71	173	2	24	16	72	23	3	23	14	71	8	5	22	13	70	Guatemala City	**Guatemala**
1327	2	28	22	85	1255	2	27	22	88	692	4	29	22	82	346	5	30	22	75	121	6	31	23	73	24	5	31	23	65	Conakry	**Guinea**
494	5	30	23	77	617	4	29	23	81	416	5	30	23	76	199	7	31	23	69	44	8	32	22	58	13	8	31	19	41	Bissau	**Guinea-Bissau**
254	9	29	24	74	175	8	30	24	73	81	8	31	24	69	76	7	31	24	69	155	7	30	24	69	287	6	29	24	75	Georgetown	**Guyana**
74	9	34	23	43	145	9	34	23	49	175	8	33	23	54	170	8	32	22	56	86	7	31	22	54	33	7	31	21	48	Port-au-Prince	**Haiti**
70	8	27	18	*	74	8	28	17	*	151	6	28	17	*	87	7	27	17	*	38	7	26	16	*	14	8	25	15	*	Tegucigalpa	**Honduras**
381	8	31	26	77	367	6	31	26	77	257	6	29	25	72	114	7	27	23	63	43	7	23	18	60	31	6	20	15	63	Hong Kong	**Hong Kong**
56	10	28	16	47	47	9	27	16	47	33	7	23	12	49	57	5	16	7	60	70	2	8	3	76	46	1	4	-1	81	Budapest	**Hungary**
50	6	14	9	72	56	5	14	8	71	67	4	11	6	73	94	2	7	3	78	78	1	4	0	80	79	0	2	-2	80	Reykjavik	**Iceland**
617	2	29	25	83	340	3	29	24	81	264	5	29	24	81	82	6	32	24	71	13	6	32	23	64	3	9	31	21	62	Bombay	**India**
325	8	29	25	83	328	4	32	26	82	252	5	32	26	81	114	7	32	24	72	20	6	31	21	69	5	8	26	13	55	Calcutta	
180	6	36	27	59	173	6	34	26	64	117	7	34	24	51	10	9	34	18	32	3	10	29	11	31	10	9	23	8	42	Delhi	
793	2	29	24	87	404	3	28	24	88	241	5	28	24	84	97	8	29	24	77	33	9	30	23	64	5	9	29	21	60	Goa	
91	5	36	26	62	117	6	35	26	66	119	7	34	25	70	305	5	32	24	75	356	5	29	22	75	140	6	29	21	72	Madras	
58	8	31	18	46	61	8	31	18	49	38	8	28	12	43	31	8	22	5	48	10	7	16	-1	51	33	5	9	-2	63	Srinagar	

Rain mm Average monthly rainfall **Sun hrs** Average daily hours of sunshine **Temp °C** Average daily maximum/minimum temperature
Hum % Average midday humidity ★ Figures not available

°C	-40	-30	-20	-10	0	10	20	30	40	°C
°F	-40 -30 -20 -10	0 10 20 30	40 50 60	70 80	90 100 110					°F

Temperature Conversion Scale

Weather Statistics

Country	Location	January Rain mm	Sun hrs	Temp °C max	min	Hum %	February Rain mm	Sun hrs	Temp °C max	min	Hum %	March Rain mm	Sun hrs	Temp °C max	min	Hum %	April Rain mm	Sun hrs	Temp °C max	min	Hum %	May Rain mm	Sun hrs	Temp °C max	min	Hum %	June Rain mm	Sun hrs	Temp °C max	min	Hum %
Indonesia	Bali	223	8	32	25	78	275	10	32	25	78	210	10	32	25	79	135	10	32	25	78	93	9	32	25	75	55	9	31	24	72
	Jakarta	300	5	29	23	75	300	5	29	23	75	211	6	30	23	73	147	7	31	24	71	114	7	31	24	69	97	7	31	23	67
	Medan	137	4	29	22	66	91	3	31	22	61	104	4	31	22	61	132	5	32	23	62	175	8	32	23	63	132	5	32	22	63
Iran	Tehran	46	6	7	-3	75	38	7	10	0	59	46	7	15	4	39	36	7	22	9	40	13	9	28	14	47	3	12	34	19	49
Iraq	Baghdad	23	6	16	4	51	25	7	18	6	42	28	8	22	9	36	13	9	29	14	34	3	10	36	19	19	0	12	41	23	13
Ireland	Cork	119	2	9	2	*	79	3	9	3	*	94	3	11	4	*	81	5	13	5	*	78	6	16	7	*	79	6	19	10	*
	Dublin	67	2	8	1	80	55	3	8	2	76	51	3	10	3	72	45	5	13	4	67	60	6	15	6	69	57	6	18	9	69
Israel	Eilat	0	7	21	10	39	8	8	23	11	40	8	8	26	14	38	5	9	31	18	30	0	10	36	17	28	0	11	38	24	20
	Jerusalem	132	6	13	5	66	132	7	13	6	58	64	7	18	8	57	28	10	23	10	42	3	11	27	14	33	0	14	29	16	32
Italy	Milan	44	2	5	0	82	60	3	8	2	73	77	5	13	6	65	94	6	18	10	57	76	7	23	14	59	118	8	27	17	56
	Naples	116	4	12	4	68	85	4	13	5	67	73	5	15	6	62	62	7	18	9	61	44	8	22	12	63	31	9	26	16	58
	Rome	71	4	11	5	68	62	4	13	5	64	57	5	15	7	56	51	7	19	10	54	46	8	23	13	54	37	9	28	17	48
	Venice	37	3	6	1	76	48	4	8	2	76	61	5	12	5	68	78	6	17	10	67	65	8	21	14	69	69	9	25	17	65
	Sardinia - Cagliari	50	4	14	7	73	50	4	15	7	69	45	6	17	9	66	31	7	19	11	65	26	9	23	14	65	13	9	27	18	58
	Sicily - Palermo	71	4	16	8	67	43	5	16	8	63	50	6	17	9	60	49	7	20	11	60	19	8	24	14	58	9	10	27	18	54
Ivory Coast	Abidjan	31	6	30	23	74	56	7	31	24	74	114	7	31	24	73	167	7	31	24	73	312	6	30	24	76	683	4	29	23	82
Jamaica	Kingston	23	8	30	19	61	15	9	30	19	62	23	9	30	20	62	31	9	31	21	66	102	8	31	22	68	89	8	32	23	68
Japan	Sapporo	89	3	-2	-12	70	64	4	-1	-11	67	61	5	2	-7	66	56	7	11	0	59	69	7	16	4	61	71	7	21	10	68
	Tokyo	48	6	8	-2	48	74	6	9	-1	48	107	6	12	2	53	135	7	17	8	59	147	6	22	12	62	165	5	24	17	68
Jordan	Amman	69	7	12	4	56	74	7	13	4	52	31	8	16	6	44	15	10	23	9	34	5	11	28	14	28	0	13	31	16	28
Kazakhstan	Alma-Ata	33	4	-5	-14	72	23	4	-3	-13	69	56	5	4	-6	66	102	7	13	3	53	94	8	20	10	49	66	9	24	14	48
Kenya	Mombasa	17	8	32	23	62	10	9	32	24	61	30	9	33	24	63	108	8	31	24	69	149	6	29	23	72	54	8	29	22	68
	Nairobi	49	9	27	13	42	36	9	28	13	38	85	9	28	14	43	153	7	26	15	53	126	6	25	14	58	32	6	24	12	54
Korea, North	Pyongyang	15	6	-3	-13	74	11	7	1	-10	70	25	7	7	-4	66	46	8	16	3	63	67	8	22	9	66	76	7	26	15	71
Korea, South	Seoul	31	6	0	-9	51	20	7	3	-7	47	38	7	8	-2	46	76	7	17	5	46	81	8	22	11	51	130	7	27	16	54
Kuwait	Kuwait	23	8	16	9	61	23	9	18	11	61	28	9	22	15	61	5	8	28	20	55	0	10	34	25	55	0	10	37	28	49
Laos	Vientiane	5	8	28	14	52	15	8	30	17	44	38	7	33	19	40	99	8	34	23	49	267	7	32	23	60	302	5	32	24	67
Latvia	Riga	31	1	-4	-10	79	29	2	-3	-10	74	27	4	2	-7	69	33	6	10	1	61	44	7	16	6	59	45	11	21	9	53
Lebanon	Beirut	191	5	17	11	70	158	5	17	11	70	94	6	19	12	69	56	8	22	14	67	18	10	26	18	64	3	12	28	21	61
Lesotho	Maseru	114	9	28	14	37	89	9	27	14	42	96	8	25	12	43	67	8	21	8	42	29	8	18	3	38	12	8	15	0	35
Liberia	Monrovia	37	6	29	23	84	56	6	29	23	87	94	7	30	24	86	164	6	30	23	86	182	5	30	23	87	934	4	29	23	89
Libya	Tripoli	54	5	19	9	59	30	6	19	9	57	19	6	21	11	59	22	7	23	13	58	3	8	26	16	59	1	10	30	19	61
Liechtenstein	Vaduz	75	2	2	-3	74	70	3	5	-2	65	65	5	10	1	55	75	6	15	4	51	100	7	19	8	52	130	7	23	12	52
Lithuania	Vilnius	30	1	-5	-11	84	39	2	-3	-10	79	38	4	1	-7	73	41	6	12	2	63	85	7	18	7	59	67	10	21	11	56
Luxembourg	Luxembourg	61	1	3	-1	86	65	2	4	-1	78	42	5	10	1	64	47	6	14	4	58	64	6	18	8	53	64	6	21	11	61
Macao	Macao	33	5	16	11	66	46	3	15	11	73	74	3	17	14	74	137	3	22	17	77	292	5	26	21	78	394	6	27	24	77
Madagascar	Antananarivo	265	7	25	16	65	206	8	25	16	65	217	7	25	16	66	41	8	24	14	60	14	7	22	12	59	10	7	20	10	59
Malawi	Lilongwe	216	5	27	17	65	199	5	27	18	66	114	6	27	16	59	44	8	27	14	53	4	8	25	11	43	2	8	24	8	40
Malaysia	Kuala Lumpur	158	6	32	22	60	201	7	33	22	60	259	7	33	23	58	292	6	33	23	63	224	6	33	23	66	130	7	33	22	63
	Kuching	610	4	29	22	75	510	4	30	22	74	328	5	31	23	73	279	6	32	23	71	262	6	32	23	70	180	6	33	23	66
	Penang	94	8	32	23	68	79	8	33	23	64	142	8	33	23	64	188	6	33	24	66	272	7	32	23	66	196	7	32	23	67
Maldives	Male Atoll	46	8	29	23	73	18	7	29	24	75	23	9	30	25	74	58	8	31	27	74	178	7	31	26	77	295	7	30	25	81
Mali	Bamako	1	9	33	16	20	1	9	36	19	16	5	9	38	22	18	16	8	39	24	27	60	8	38	25	42	150	8	35	23	58
Malta	Valletta	90	5	14	10	67	60	6	15	10	66	39	7	16	11	65	15	9	18	13	64	12	10	22	16	63	2	11	26	19	60
Martinique	Fort-de-France	119	8	28	21	77	109	8	29	21	73	74	9	29	21	72	99	8	30	22	71	119	8	31	23	74	188	7	30	23	77
Mauritania	Nouakchott	1	8	29	13	30	2	9	31	15	27	1	10	33	16	29	1	10	34	18	30	1	9	34	19	35	1	10	34	22	45
Mauritius	Port Louis	176	8	30	23	74	203	8	30	23	72	245	7	30	23	75	163	8	29	21	70	83	8	27	19	73	65	7	25	17	72
Mexico	Acapulco	8	9	31	22	77	1	9	32	22	76	1	9	32	22	74	1	8	31	23	76	39	7	32	24	75	277	7	32	25	77
	Cancun	28	5	28	19	74	25	5	29	19	71	17	6	31	20	67	21	6	33	22	67	85	7	33	23	70	137	6	33	23	77
	Mexico City	8	7	21	5	32	4	8	24	6	29	9	8	26	7	23	23	8	27	9	26	57	7	27	10	34	11	7	25	11	41
	Monterrey	17	5	20	10	66	17	5	23	11	64	11	6	26	14	55	27	5	30	18	61	36	6	31	21	66	49	8	33	22	62
Moldova	Kishinev	56	2	-1	-8	76	50	2	1	-5	75	42	4	6	-2	62	35	7	16	6	41	34	9	23	11	41	68	9	26	14	47
Monaco	Monte Carlo	61	5	12	8	67	58	5	13	8	69	71	5	14	10	73	65	6	16	12	72	64	7	19	15	75	33	8	23	19	75
Mongolia	Ulan Bator	0	3	-19	-32	73	0	4	-13	-29	66	3	5	-4	-22	61	5	7	7	-8	42	10	8	13	-2	40	28	7	21	7	44
Montserrat	Plymouth	122	7	28	21	65	86	7	28	21	61	112	7	29	21	59	89	8	30	22	59	97	8	31	23	60	112	7	31	24	63
Morocco	Casablanca	78	5	17	8	72	61	6	18	9	72	54	7	20	11	68	37	9	21	12	67	20	9	22	15	67	3	10	24	18	63
	Marrakech	29	7	18	5	63	31	7	20	7	59	31	8	23	9	55	33	9	25	12	53	20	9	29	14	47	8	11	33	17	48
	Rabat	86	5	17	8	72	65	5	18	8	69	67	7	20	10	68*	49	9	22	11	64	21	9	23	14	64	7	10	25	16	66
Mozambique	Maputo	141	8	30	22	68	137	8	30	22	68	89	8	29	21	67	63	8	28	19	66	28	8	27	16	63	28	8	25	14	60
Myanmar	Mandalay	3	9	28	13	52	3	9	31	15	41	5	9	36	19	31	31	9	38	25	33	147	8	37	26	52	160	6	34	26	64
	Yangon	3	10	32	18	52	5	10	33	19	52	8	10	36	22	54	51	10	36	24	64	307	7	33	25	76	480	4	30	24	85
Namibia	Windhoek	71	9	30	17	26	76	9	29	17	25	77	8	27	15	36	41	9	26	13	29	5	10	23	9	22	2	10	20	7	21
Nepal	Kathmandu	15	6	18	2	70	41	6	19	4	68	23	8	25	7	53	58	6	28	12	54	122	5	30	16	61	246	2	29	19	72

Rain mm Average monthly rainfall **Sun hrs** Average daily hours of sunshine **Temp °C** Average daily maximum/minimum temperature
Hum % Average midday humidity ＊ Figures not available

Rainfall Conversion Scale

mm	5	25	50	75	100	150	200	300	600	1200
in	0.2	1	2	3	4	6	8	12	24	48

July Rain mm	Sun hrs	Temp °C max	min	Hum %	Aug Rain mm	Sun hrs	Temp °C max	min	Hum %	Sep Rain mm	Sun hrs	Temp °C max	min	Hum %	Oct Rain mm	Sun hrs	Temp °C max	min	Hum %	Nov Rain mm	Sun hrs	Temp °C max	min	Hum %	Dec Rain mm	Sun hrs	Temp °C max	min	Hum %	Location	Country
25	9	31	24	68	5	10	31	24	66	5	11	32	25	65	18	10	33	26	64	60	10	33	26	68	163	10	32	25	74	Bali	Indonesia
64	7	31	23	64	43	8	31	23	61	66	8	31	23	62	112	7	31	23	64	142	6	30	23	68	203	5	29	23	71	Jakarta	
135	6	32	22	59	178	6	32	22	61	211	7	31	22	66	259	9	30	22	69	246	8	30	22	69	229	5	29	22	68	Medan	
3	11	37	22	24	3	11	36	22	46	3	10	32	18	49	8	8	24	12	54	20	7	17	6	66	31	6	11	1	75	Tehran	Iran
0	11	43	24	12	0	11	43	24	13	0	11	40	21	15	3	9	33	16	22	20	7	25	11	39	25	6	18	6	52	Baghdad	Iraq
80	5	20	12	*	83	5	20	12	*	86	4	18	10	*	90	3	14	7	*	90	2	11	4	*	89	2	9	3	*	Cork	Ireland
70	5	20	11	70	74	5	19	11	72	72	4	17	9	73	70	3	14	6	75	67	2	10	4	79	74	2	8	3	81	Dublin	
0	11	39	26	13	0	11	40	26	24	0	10	37	25	27	0	9	33	21	34	0	8	26	16	38	8	7	23	12	42	Eilat	Israel
0	13	31	17	35	0	13	31	18	36	0	11	29	17	36	13	7	27	15	36	71	7	21	12	50	86	6	15	7	60	Jerusalem	
64	9	29	20	61	91	8	28	19	58	69	6	24	16	63	125	4	17	11	73	122	2	10	6	80	77	2	6	2	89	Milan	Italy
19	10	29	18	53	32	10	29	18	53	64	8	26	16	59	107	6	22	12	63	147	4	17	9	68	135	3	14	6	70	Naples	
15	11	30	20	42	21	10	30	19	43	63	8	26	17	50	99	6	22	13	59	129	4	16	9	66	93	4	13	6	70	Rome	
52	10	27	19	64	69	8	27	18	63	59	7	24	16	64	77	5	19	11	68	94	2	12	7	75	61	3	8	3	79	Venice	
1	11	30	21	58	10	10	30	21	61	32	8	27	19	61	54	6	23	15	64	72	4	19	11	67	67	3	16	9	73	Cagliari - Sardinia	
2	10	30	21	52	18	9	30	21	52	41	8	28	19	53	77	6	25	16	61	71	6	21	12	64	62	4	18	10	65	Palermo - Sicily	
274	4	28	23	79	38	4	27	22	80	55	4	28	22	81	194	6	29	23	79	174	7	30	24	75	113	7	30	24	74	Abidjan	Ivory Coast
89	9	32	23	65	91	8	32	23	70	99	8	32	23	70	180	7	31	23	73	74	8	31	22	68	36	8	31	21	62	Kingston	Jamaica
84	6	24	14	71	94	6	26	16	69	127	6	22	11	67	117	5	16	4	63	112	4	8	-2	66	102	3	1	-8	68	Sapporo	Japan
142	6	29	22	76	152	7	30	22	66	234	5	26	19	72	208	4	21	13	64	97	5	16	6	58	56	5	11	1	51	Tokyo	
0	13	32	18	30	0	13	32	18	30	0	11	31	17	31	5	10	27	14	31	33	8	21	10	40	46	6	15	6	53	Amman	Jordan
36	10	27	16	43	31	10	27	14	39	25	8	22	8	39	51	6	13	2	49	48	4	4	-5	67	33	4	-2	-9	72	Alma-Ata	Kazakhstan
34	7	28	21	68	47	8	28	21	68	46	9	29	21	65	62	9	30	22	66	66	9	31	23	68	32	9	32	24	66	Mombasa	Kenya
13	4	23	11	55	18	4	23	12	53	21	6	26	12	44	48	7	27	13	42	132	7	25	14	53	75	8	25	14	50	Nairobi	
237	6	29	20	80	228	7	29	20	80	112	7	24	14	75	45	8	18	6	73	41	6	9	-2	73	21	6	0	-10	74	Pyongyang	Korea, North
376	6	29	21	67	267	7	31	22	62	119	7	26	15	54	41	8	19	7	48	46	6	11	0	52	25	6	3	-7	52	Seoul	Korea, South
0	10	39	30	41	0	11	40	30	46	0	10	38	27	51	3	10	33	23	60	15	8	25	17	59	28	7	18	12	65	Kuwait	Kuwait
267	5	31	24	69	292	5	31	24	73	302	8	31	24	72	109	8	31	21	69	15	8	29	18	63	3	8	28	16	57	Vientiane	Laos
53	10	22	11	55	70	9	21	11	59	64	6	17	8	64	62	3	11	4	75	62	1	4	-1	78	47	1	-2	-7	84	Riga	Latvia
0	12	31	23	58	0	11	32	23	57	5	9	30	23	57	51	8	27	21	62	132	7	23	16	64	185	5	18	13	69	Beirut	Lebanon
14	8	16	-1	32	15	9	19	2	27	19	9	23	6	24	63	9	24	9	30	80	9	26	12	34	93	10	28	13	35	Maseru	Lesotho
822	3	27	23	89	442	3	27	23	89	684	6	28	22	89	633	4	29	23	88	237	6	30	23	86	126	5	29	23	86	Monrovia	Liberia
0	11	32	21	62	0	11	32	21	62	13	8	31	20	64	34	6	28	17	61	34	5	25	13	57	74	5	20	10	59	Tripoli	Libya
135	8	25	14	52	125	7	24	13	53	100	6	20	11	57	75	5	14	6	64	75	2	7	2	73	65	1	3	-2	76	Vaduz	Liechtenstein
51	10	23	12	56	97	9	22	12	57	61	6	17	8	62	49	3	11	4	78	65	1	4	-1	85	39	1	-3	-7	88	Vilnius	Lithuania
60	6	23	13	61	84	6	22	12	63	72	5	19	10	67	53	3	13	6	76	67	1	7	3	86	81	1	4	0	91	Luxembourg	Luxembourg
381	8	29	24	77	367	7	29	24	77	257	6	27	23	72	114	7	25	21	63	43	6	21	16	60	31	6	18	13	63	Macao	Macao
11	7	19	9	58	13	7	20	9	56	12	9	22	10	50	45	9	25	12	49	161	8	26	14	54	293	6	25	15	61	Antananarivo	Madagascar
1	8	24	8	38	1	8	25	9	36	7	9	28	12	33	4	10	30	15	32	60	7	30	17	43	171	5	27	18	61	Lilongwe	Malawi
99	6	32	23	63	163	6	32	23	62	218	6	32	23	64	249	5	32	23	65	259	5	32	23	66	191	5	32	22	61	Kuala Lumpur	Malaysia
196	6	32	22	66	234	5	33	22	68	218	5	32	22	70	267	4	32	23	71	358	5	31	22	74	462	4	31	22	75	Kuching	
191	7	32	23	67	295	6	32	23	67	401	5	32	23	70	429	5	32	23	70	302	6	31	23	71	147	7	32	23	68	Penang	
226	7	29	24	82	198	7	29	25	79	160	7	29	25	79	185	6	29	24	78	140	8	29	23	79	86	7	29	23	80	Male Atoll	Maldives
246	7	32	22	69	311	5	30	22	74	230	7	31	21	69	70	8	34	21	54	8	8	35	18	32	1	8	33	16	24	Bamako	Mali
0	12	29	22	59	8	11	29	23	62	29	9	27	22	62	63	7	24	19	65	91	6	17	14	68	110	5	16	12	68	Valletta	Malta
239	8	30	23	78	262	8	31	23	78	236	8	31	23	79	246	7	31	23	80	201	8	30	22	81	150	8	29	22	79	Fort-de-France	Martinique
15	9	32	24	59	61	9	33	25	64	47	9	35	25	59	10	9	36	22	39	4	9	34	18	29	10	8	29	14	31	Nouakchott	Mauritania
63	7	25	17	70	58	7	25	17	66	38	7	26	17	64	9	7	27	18	62	79	7	29	20	65	128	9	30	21	66	Port Louis	Mauritius
282	7	32	17	57	222	7	33	25	78	384	6	32	25	81	157	7	32	25	80	34	9	32	24	78	11	9	31	23	78	Acapulco	Mexico
129	6	33	23	79	149	6	33	23	79	183	5	32	23	80	94	5	30	22	79	34	5	29	20	76	35	5	28	19	76	Cancun	
160	6	23	11	55	149	6	24	11	50	119	6	23	11	58	46	6	22	9	48	16	7	21	6	38	7	7	21	5	36	Mexico City	
59	7	34	23	66	119	6	33	23	67	156	6	30	21	73	93	6	31	17	70	23	6	28	13	68	13	4	20	10	66	Monterrey	
65	9	27	16	48	38	9	27	15	46	45	7	23	11	47	22	6	17	7	52	39	2	10	3	71	45	1	2	-4	76	Kishinev	Moldova
21	9	26	22	71	22	9	26	22	72	66	7	24	20	71	113	6	20	16	71	123	5	16	12	72	99	4	14	10	72	Monte Carlo	Monaco
76	7	22	11	54	51	7	21	8	49	23	6	14	2	43	5	5	6	-8	48	5	3	-6	-20	57	3	2	-16	-28	75	Ulan Bator	Mongolia
155	8	31	24	64	183	8	31	24	66	168	7	32	23	66	196	8	31	23	66	180	7	29	23	68	140	7	28	22	67	Plymouth	Montserrat
1	10	26	19	71	1	10	26	20	72	6	9	26	18	70	28	7	24	15	65	58	6	21	12	66	94	5	18	10	71	Casablanca	Morocco
2	11	38	20	39	3	11	37	20	40	10	10	33	18	45	17	8	28	15	52	34	7	23	10	59	34	7	19	7	61	Marrakech	
1	11	28	18	66	2	10	28	18	65	9	9	27	17	65	35	8	25	15	62	91	6	21	12	66	103	5	18	9	70	Rabat	
18	8	25	14	61	18	8	25	15	62	37	8	26	17	66	77	7	27	18	70	78	7	28	20	70	87	7	29	29	69	Maputo	Mozambique
69	5	34	26	66	104	4	33	25	72	137	6	33	24	74	109	7	32	23	78	51	8	29	19	74	10	9	27	14	66	Mandalay	Myanmar
582	3	29	24	89	528	3	29	24	88	394	5	30	24	77	66	8	31	24	77	6	8	32	13	69	18	8	31	19	61	Yangon	
1	10	21	7	17	1	11	24	9	13	3	10	27	12	11	13	10	29	15	13	35	10	30	16	20	39	10	30	17	21	Windhoek	Namibia
373	2	29	20	82	345	3	28	20	84	155	5	28	19	83	38	10	27	13	81	8	10	23	7	78	3	9	19	3	73	Kathmandu	Nepal

Rain mm Average monthly rainfall **Sun hrs** Average daily hours of sunshine **Temp °C** Average daily maximum/minimum temperature **Hum %** Average midday humidity ★ Figures not available

°C	-40	-30	-20	-10	0	10	20	30	40	°C
°F	-40	-30 -20 -10	0	10 20	30	40 50 60	70	80 90 100	110	°F

Temperature Conversion Scale

Country	Location	Jan Rain mm	Jan Sun hrs	Jan Temp max	Jan Temp min	Jan Hum %	Feb Rain mm	Feb Sun hrs	Feb Temp max	Feb Temp min	Feb Hum %	Mar Rain mm	Mar Sun hrs	Mar Temp max	Mar Temp min	Mar Hum %	Apr Rain mm	Apr Sun hrs	Apr Temp max	Apr Temp min	Apr Hum %	May Rain mm	May Sun hrs	May Temp max	May Temp min	May Hum %	Jun Rain mm	Jun Sun hrs	Jun Temp max	Jun Temp min	Jun Hum %
Netherlands	Amsterdam	68	2	4	-1	82	53	2	5	-1	76	44	4	10	1	65	49	5	13	4	61	52	7	18	8	59	58	7	21	11	59
Neth Antilles	Curaçao	53	8	28	24	69	25	9	29	23	68	20	9	29	23	66	28	8	30	24	67	20	7	30	25	68	25	8	31	26	68
New Caledonia	Nouméa	94	8	30	22	70	130	8	29	23	72	145	7	29	22	73	132	7	28	21	74	112	6	26	19	71	94	6	25	18	70
New Zealand	Auckland	79	7	23	16	62	94	7	23	16	61	81	6	22	15	65	97	5	19	13	69	127	4	17	11	70	137	4	14	9	73
	Christchurch	56	7	21	12	59	43	7	21	12	60	48	5	19	10	69	48	5	17	7	71	66	4	13	4	69	66	4	11	2	72
	Wellington	81	8	21	13	67	81	7	21	13	71	81	6	19	12	69	97	5	17	11	76	117	4	13	8	77	117	4	13	7	78
Nicaragua	Managua	5	7	31	20	*	1	8	32	21	*	5	8	34	22	*	5	7	34	23	*	76	6	34	23	*	296	4	31	23	*
Niger	Niamey	1	9	33	16	13	0	9	36	18	11	2	9	39	22	11	6	8	41	26	19	33	9	40	27	34	77	9	37	25	45
Nigeria	Lagos	28	6	32	22	64	40	7	33	23	61	95	6	33	23	67	134	6	32	23	70	225	6	31	23	75	349	5	27	22	82
Norway	Bergen	143	1	3	-1	77	142	2	3	-1	74	109	3	6	0	67	139	5	9	3	68	83	6	14	7	64	126	6	16	10	71
	Oslo	49	1	-2	-7	82	35	3	-1	-7	74	26	5	4	-4	64	43	6	10	1	57	44	8	16	6	52	70	8	20	10	55
Oman	Muscat	28	9	25	19	71	18	10	25	19	73	10	9	28	22	70	10	11	32	26	68	0	12	37	30	60	3	12	38	31	72
Pakistan	Islamabad	64	7	16	2	44	64	8	19	6	46	81	8	24	10	37	42	10	31	15	26	23	10	37	21	19	55	9	40	25	23
	Karachi	13	9	25	13	45	10	9	26	14	49	8	9	29	19	57	3	10	32	23	62	3	10	34	26	68	18	8	34	28	69
Panama	Panama City	25	8	31	22	*	10	8	32	22	*	18	9	32	22	*	74	8	31	23	*	203	6	30	23	*	213	5	31	23	*
Papua N Guinea	Port Moresby	178	6	32	24	69	193	5	31	24	72	170	6	31	24	73	107	7	31	24	74	64	7	30	24	77	33	7	29	23	77
Paraguay	Asunción	140	9	35	22	56	130	9	34	22	55	109	8	33	21	55	132	8	29	18	59	117	7	25	14	62	69	6	22	12	61
Peru	Lima	3	6	28	19	69	0	7	28	19	66	0	7	28	19	64	0	7	27	17	66	5	4	23	16	76	5	1	20	14	80
Philippines	Manila	23	6	30	21	63	13	7	31	21	59	18	7	33	22	55	33	9	34	23	55	130	7	34	24	61	254	5	33	24	68
Poland	Warsaw	27	2	0	-6	84	32	2	0	-6	80	27	3	6	-2	70	37	5	12	3	61	46	8	20	9	56	69	8	23	12	59
Portugal	Algarve	70	6	15	9	72	52	7	16	10	70	72	7	18	11	72	31	9	20	13	67	21	10	22	14	67	5	12	25	18	65
	Lisbon	111	5	14	8	71	76	7	15	8	64	109	7	17	10	64	54	9	20	12	56	44	10	21	13	57	16	11	25	15	54
	Oporto	159	5	13	5	69	112	6	14	5	65	147	6	16	8	65	86	8	18	9	61	87	9	20	11	65	41	10	23	13	64
Azores - Ponta Delgada		143	3	16	12	80	113	3	16	12	80	150	4	16	12	79	77	5	17	12	77	70	5	18	14	76	49	6	21	16	77
Madeira - Funchal		99	5	19	13	66	95	6	19	13	67	74	6	19	13	68	40	7	20	14	68	18	7	21	15	69	10	7	22	17	72
Puerto Rico	San Juan	109	7	27	21	75	69	8	27	21	74	74	9	27	21	74	104	9	28	22	75	150	8	29	23	75	137	8	29	24	77
Qatar	Doha	8	8	20	14	71	18	8	21	15	70	13	8	24	17	70	8	9	29	21	66	0	10	33	26	63	0	11	36	28	64
Réunion	St Denis	263	8	30	23	72	216	8	30	23	73	290	7	29	23	75	160	7	28	21	69	81	8	27	20	67	75	7	26	18	64
Romania	Bucharest	46	2	1	-7	87	26	3	4	-5	84	28	5	10	-1	73	59	6	18	5	63	77	8	23	10	63	121	9	27	14	62
Russia	Moscow	39	1	-9	-16	77	38	3	-6	-14	66	36	4	0	-8	64	37	5	10	1	54	53	8	19	8	43	58	9	21	11	47
	St Petersburg	35	0	-7	-13	84	30	2	-5	-12	73	31	4	0	-8	70	36	5	8	0	65	45	8	15	6	57	50	10	20	11	53
	Tomsk	28	2	-18	-24	78	18	3	-13	-22	70	20	5	-6	-17	61	23	7	-3	-7	55	41	9	12	3	50	66	10	19	9	55
	Vladivostok	8	6	-11	-18	58	10	7	-6	-14	55	18	7	1	-9	56	31	6	8	1	59	53	6	13	6	65	74	5	17	11	76
Rwanda	Kigali	96	5	26	15	*	82	4	26	15	*	103	5	26	15	*	177	5	25	15	*	132	5	25	15	*	24	7	25	15	*
St Kitts & Nevis	St Kitts	104	8	27	22	69	51	8	27	21	66	58	9	28	22	65	58	9	28	25	67	97	9	29	24	71	91	9	29	24	71
St Lucia	Castries	135	8	28	21	70	91	8	28	21	68	97	9	29	21	65	86	8	31	22	64	150	8	31	23	65	218	7	31	23	69
St Vincent	St Vincent	140	9	29	17	70	108	9	29	17	68	107	7	31	18	65	96	8	32	19	64	160	8	33	20	65	228	7	33	21	69
Saudi Arabia	Riyadh	3	7	21	8	44	20	8	23	9	37	23	7	28	13	36	25	8	32	18	34	10	9	38	22	31	0	11	42	25	31
Senegal	Dakar	1	8	25	17	55	2	9	25	17	60	0	10	25	17	63	1	10	25	18	67	1	10	26	20	70	9	9	29	23	69
Seychelles	Mahe	331	6	28	25	79	266	6	29	25	77	241	7	30	25	75	172	8	31	25	74	136	8	30	25	74	83	7	28	25	75
Sierra Leone	Freetown	11	8	29	24	70	8	8	30	24	69	18	8	30	25	71	59	7	30	25	72	160	6	30	25	75	351	5	30	24	78
Singapore	Singapore	252	5	30	23	78	173	7	31	23	71	193	6	31	24	70	188	6	31	24	74	173	6	32	24	73	173	6	31	24	73
Slovakia	Bratislava	43	2	2	-3	77	47	3	3	-2	70	42	5	9	1	58	42	7	16	6	49	61	9	21	11	49	64	9	24	14	50
Slovenia	Ljubljana	88	2	2	-4	81	89	3	5	-4	70	76	4	10	0	60	98	5	15	4	56	121	6	20	9	56	133	7	24	12	56
Solomon Islands	Honiara	267	6	31	24	79	272	5	31	24	79	285	5	31	24	78	297	6	31	24	80	236	7	31	24	79	229	6	30	24	81
Somalia	Mogadishu	1	8	29	23	78	1	9	29	23	75	6	9	31	26	75	57	8	32	27	75	54	8	31	26	77	82	7	29	24	79
South Africa	Cape Town	12	11	26	15	52	19	10	26	15	53	17	9	25	14	52	42	8	23	11	55	67	6	20	9	63	98	6	18	7	63
	Durban	131	6	28	21	71	114	7	28	21	70	136	7	28	20	68	108	7	26	17	66	54	7	24	13	61	32	8	23	10	55
	Johannesburg	112	8	25	14	50	97	8	25	14	52	75	8	24	13	49	61	8	21	10	48	22	9	19	7	39	9	9	16	4	35
Spain	Barcelona	31	5	13	6	61	39	6	14	7	58	48	6	16	9	60	43	7	18	11	58	54	8	21	14	59	37	9	25	18	59
	Madrid	39	5	9	2	71	34	6	11	2	62	43	6	15	5	56	48	8	18	7	49	47	9	21	10	49	27	11	27	15	41
	Malaga	61	6	17	8	64	51	6	17	9	65	62	6	18	11	64	46	8	21	13	62	26	10	23	15	61	9	11	27	19	61
	Seville	66	6	15	6	75	61	6	17	7	69	90	6	20	9	67	57	8	24	11	61	41	9	27	13	57	8	11	32	17	48
	Valencia	32	5	15	5	58	32	6	16	6	59	30	6	18	8	55	31	7	20	10	55	31	8	23	13	59	25	9	26	17	59
Ibiza - Ibiza		42	5	15	7	66	35	6	15	7	66	25	6	16	9	65	22	8	19	11	61	13	10	22	14	61	22	11	26	18	60
Majorca - Palma		39	5	14	6	72	34	6	15	6	70	51	6	17	8	66	32	7	19	10	66	29	10	22	13	67	17	10	26	17	65
Minorca - Mahon		62	4	14	7	71	49	5	14	7	70	51	6	15	8	67	41	6	17	10	67	29	9	21	13	63	17	10	24	16	60
Gran Canaria - Las Palmas		20	6	21	14	66	18	6	22	13	66	11	7	22	14	65	7	8	22	15	63	2	8	23	16	65	1	9	25	18	66
Tenerife - Santa Cruz		44	6	21	15	63	33	6	21	14	61	27	7	22	15	60	12	8	23	16	56	6	9	24	17	57	1	10	26	19	56
Sri Lanka	Colombo	89	8	30	22	67	69	9	31	22	66	147	8	31	23	66	231	7	31	24	70	371	6	31	26	76	224	5	29	25	78
Sudan	Khartoum	0	11	32	16	21	0	11	33	17	16	0	10	37	20	13	1	11	40	23	13	7	10	42	26	14	5	10	41	27	18
Surinam	Paramaribo	213	6	29	22	77	165	6	29	22	75	201	6	29	22	75	229	6	30	23	79	310	5	30	23	79	302	6	30	23	80
Swaziland	Mbabane	228	8	25	15	52	213	8	25	15	50	147	8	24	14	46	101	7	23	12	45	28	8	21	8	33	16	8	19	5	32

Rain mm Average monthly rainfall **Sun hrs** Average daily hours of sunshine **Temp °C** Average daily maximum/minimum temperature
Hum % Average midday humidity * Figures not available

Rainfall Conversion Scale

mm	5	25	50	75	100	150	200	300	600	1200
in	0.2	1	2	3	4	6	8	12	24	48

July					August					September					October					November					December					Location	Country
Rain mm	Sun hrs	Temp °C max	min	Hum %	Rain mm	Sun hrs	Temp °C max	min	Hum %	Rain mm	Sun hrs	Temp °C max	min	Hum %	Rain mm	Sun hrs	Temp °C max	min	Hum %	Rain mm	Sun hrs	Temp °C max	min	Hum %	Rain mm	Sun hrs	Temp °C max	min	Hum %		
77	6	22	13	64	87	6	22	13	65	72	5	19	10	67	72	3	14	7	72	70	2	9	3	81	64	1	5	1	85	Amsterdam	**Netherlands**
38	9	31	25	68	31	9	31	26	67	28	9	32	26	67	107	8	31	26	70	112	8	30	24	72	99	7	29	24	71	Curaçao	**Neth Antilles**
91	6	24	17	69	66	7	24	16	68	64	7	26	17	67	51	9	27	18	66	61	8	28	20	67	66	8	30	21	68	Nouméa	**New Caledonia**
145	4	13	8	74	117	5	14	8	70	102	5	16	9	68	102	6	17	11	66	89	7	19	12	64	79	7	21	14	64	Auckland	**New Zealand**
69	4	10	2	76	48	5	11	2	66	46	5	14	4	69	43	6	17	7	60	48	7	19	8	64	56	7	21	11	60	Christchurch	
137	3	12	6	76	117	4	12	6	74	97	5	14	8	75	102	6	16	9	74	89	7	17	10	69	89	7	19	12	69	Wellington	
134	5	31	22	*	130	6	31	22	*	182	6	31	22	*	243	6	31	22	*	59	7	31	21	*	5	6	31	20	*	Managua	**Nicaragua**
181	8	34	24	58	206	7	32	23	60	112	8	33	23	60	17	9	37	23	38	1	10	37	19	18	1	9	34	16	15	Niamey	. **Niger**
251	3	28	22	81	88	2	28	21	78	179	3	29	22	80	187	5	30	23	80	71	7	31	22	75	26	7	32	22	67	Lagos	**Nigeria**
142	6	19	12	73	168	6	19	12	73	228	3	15	10	74	235	2	11	6	76	211	1	8	3	77	204	0	5	1	79	Bergen	**Norway**
82	7	22	13	59	95	6	21	12	61	81	5	16	8	66	74	3	9	3	72	68	1	3	-1	83	63	1	0	-4	85	Oslo	
0	9	36	31	77	0	10	33	29	80	0	11	34	28	77	3	10	34	27	74	10	10	30	23	72	18	9	20	20	71	Muscat	**Oman**
233	8	36	25	45	258	9	34	24	54	85	10	34	21	44	21	9	32	15	29	8	8	28	9	26	23	7	20	3	39	Islamabad	**Pakistan**
81	4	33	27	73	41	5	31	26	74	13	7	31	25	71	0	9	33	22	57	3	9	31	18	49	5	9	27	14	45	Karachi	
180	5	31	23	*	201	5	30	23	*	208	6	29	23	*	257	5	29	23	*	259	5	29	23	*	122	7	31	23	*	Panama City	**Panama**
28	7	28	23	78	18	7	28	23	77	25	7	29	23	77	36	7	30	24	76	48	8	31	24	73	112	7	32	24	69	Port Moresby	**Papua N Guinea**
56	6	23	12	56	38	7	26	14	53	79	7	28	16	48	140	8	30	17	50	150	9	32	18	53	158	10	34	21	50	Asunción	**Paraguay**
8	1	19	14	77	8	1	19	13	78	8	1	20	14	76	3	3	22	14	72	3	4	23	16	71	0	5	26	17	70	Lima	**Peru**
432	4	31	24	74	422	4	31	24	73	356	4	31	24	73	193	5	31	23	71	145	5	31	22	69	66	5	30	21	67	Manila	**Philippines**
96	7	24	15	63	65	7	23	14	63	43	5	19	10	64	38	4	13	5	73	31	2	6	1	83	44	1	2	-3	87	Warsaw	**Poland**
1	12	28	20	62	1	12	28	20	63	17	9	26	19	66	51	7	22	16	66	65	6	19	13	70	67	6	16	10	70	Algarve	**Portugal**
3	12	27	17	48	4	12	28	17	49	33	9	26	17	54	62	7	22	14	59	93	6	17	11	68	103	5	15	9	72	Lisbon	
20	11	25	15	60	26	10	25	15	60	51	8	24	14	63	105	6	21	11	64	148	5	17	8	68	168	4	14	5	70	Oporto	
43	6	23	18	74	44	7	24	19	74	96	6	23	18	75	124	4	21	16	77	143	3	18	14	78	112	3	17	13	80	Ponta Delgada - Azores	
2	8	24	18	71	3	8	25	19	69	21	8	25	19	68	68	7	24	18	65	107	5	22	16	65	77	5	20	14	66	Funchal - Madeira	
145	8	29	24	78	160	9	29	24	77	158	7	30	24	76	142	8	29	24	76	157	7	29	23	76	137	7	27	22	77	San Juan	**Puerto Rico**
0	11	37	29	67	0	10	38	29	65	0	10	36	27	64	0	10	32	24	66	18	9	28	21	70	18	8	22	16	77	Doha	**Qatar**
70	7	25	17	66	49	7	24	17	64	47	7	25	17	65	44	7	26	19	64	95	7	27	20	67	151	7	29	22	72	St Denis	**Réunion**
53	11	30	16	58	45	10	30	15	59	45	8	25	11	63	29	5	18	6	73	36	2	10	2	85	27	2	4	-3	89	Bucharest	**Romania**
88	9	23	13	54	71	8	22	12	55	58	6	16	7	59	45	3	9	3	67	47	1	2	-3	79	54	0	-5	-10	83	Moscow	**Russia**
72	9	21	13	61	78	8	20	13	61	64	5	15	9	68	76	2	9	4	78	46	1	2	-2	85	40	0	-3	-8	86	St Petersburg	
69	10	23	12	58	66	8	20	10	63	41	6	14	4	61	51	3	3	-3	70	46	2	-9	-14	77	38	1	-16	-22	81	Tomsk	
84	4	22	16	79	119	5	24	18	74	109	7	20	13	64	48	7	13	5	53	31	6	2	-4	55	15	6	-7	-13	56	Vladivostok	
5	8	26	14	*	25	7	27	16	*	60	7	27	15	*	108	6	27	15	*	107	5	26	15	*	88	4	26	15	*	Kigali	**Rwanda**
112	9	30	24	71	132	9	30	24	72	152	8	30	24	73	137	8	29	24	73	183	8	29	23	74	114	8	28	23	72	St Kitts	**St Kitts & Nevis**
236	8	31	23	71	269	8	31	23	69	252	8	31	23	70	236	7	31	22	69	231	8	29	22	75	198	8	28	21	71	Castries	**St Lucia**
246	8	33	22	71	279	8	33	22	69	262	8	32	22	70	246	8	31	21	69	241	8	31	20	75	208	8	30	18	71	St Vincent	**St Vincent**
0	11	42	26	19	0	10	42	24	19	0	9	39	22	24	0	10	34	16	25	0	9	29	13	33	0	7	21	9	52	Riyadh	**Saudi Arabia**
96	7	30	25	71	227	6	30	25	75	174	7	30	24	75	68	8	30	24	72	2	9	29	23	61	3	8	27	20	52	Dakar	**Senegal**
59	7	28	24	76	89	7	28	24	77	118	7	28	24	76	199	7	29	24	77	200	7	29	24	75	297	6	29	24	77	Mahe	**Seychelles**
845	3	28	23	81	835	2	28	23	82	566	4	28	23	81	262	6	29	23	79	123	7	29	24	72	41	7	29	24	72	Freetown	**Sierra Leone**
170	6	31	24	72	196	6	31	24	72	178	5	31	24	72	208	5	31	23	72	254	5	31	23	75	257	4	31	23	78	Singapore	**Singapore**
73	9	26	16	49	69	9	26	16	51	40	7	22	12	52	54	5	15	7	62	55	2	8	3	76	59	1	4	0	80	Bratislava	**Slovakia**
113	8	27	14	54	127	7	26	14	55	142	5	22	11	62	151	3	15	6	70	131	1	8	2	80	114	1	4	-1	86	Ljubljana	**Slovenia**
277	6	29	23	80	239	4	29	23	80	203	7	31	23	79	207	7	31	23	79	249	6	31	24	79	239	6	32	24	76	Honiara	**Solomon Islands**
56	7	28	24	80	32	8	28	23	80	17	9	29	24	80	16	9	30	25	78	42	8	30	25	78	8	8	30	24	78	Mogadishu	**Somalia**
68	6	17	7	63	76	7	18	7	52	36	8	19	8	54	45	9	21	10	55	12	10	24	13	53	13	11	25	15	53	Cape Town	**South Africa**
37	7	23	10	58	43	7	23	12	60	61	6	23	15	66	100	6	24	17	69	113	5	25	19	72	117	6	27	20	71	Durban	
8	9	17	4	32	5	10	19	6	28	25	10	23	9	29	116	8	24	13	47	116	8	24	13	47	105	8	26	14	50	Johannesburg	
27	10	28	21	59	49	9	28	21	63	76	7	25	19	66	86	5	21	15	64	52	5	16	11	64	45	4	13	8	62	Barcelona	**Spain**
11	12	31	17	33	15	11	30	17	35	32	9	25	14	46	53	6	19	10	58	47	5	13	5	65	48	5	9	2	70	Madrid	
1	11	29	21	64	3	11	30	22	63	29	9	27	20	66	64	7	23	16	68	64	6	20	12	67	62	5	17	10	65	Malaga	
1	12	36	20	43	5	11	36	20	45	19	9	32	18	53	70	7	26	14	63	67	6	20	10	72	79	5	16	7	73	Seville	
9	10	29	20	62	26	9	29	20	63	56	7	27	18	63	75	6	23	13	60	38	5	19	10	58	37	5	16	7	58	Valencia	
5	11	28	21	59	12	11	29	22	61	34	8	27	20	63	85	6	23	15	63	102	5	19	12	66	47	5	16	9	66	Ibiza - Ibiza	
3	11	29	20	65	25	11	29	20	68	55	8	27	18	69	77	6	23	14	71	47	5	18	11	72	40	4	15	8	72	Palma - Majorca	
5	12	28	20	57	25	10	28	20	61	68	7	26	19	65	86	5	22	15	65	89	5	18	11	72	66	5	15	9	72	Mahon - Minorca	
2	9	26	20	64	1	9	27	21	64	4	8	27	20	67	9	7	26	19	66	36	6	25	17	65	29	6	22	14	66	Las Palmas - Gran Canaria	
1	11	29	20	52	1	11	29	21	54	9	8	28	20	59	33	7	26	19	62	47	6	24	17	63	55	5	21	16	62	Santa Cruz - Tenerife	
135	6	29	25	77	109	6	29	25	76	160	6	29	25	75	348	7	29	24	76	315	6	29	23	75	147	8	29	22	69	Colombo	**Sri Lanka**
56	9	38	26	31	80	9	36	25	42	28	10	38	25	30	2	10	39	25	20	0	11	35	21	21	0	11	32	17	23	Khartoum	**Sudan**
231	8	31	23	76	158	9	32	23	70	79	9	33	23	66	76	9	33	23	67	125	8	32	23	71	224	6	30	22	77	Paramaribo	**Surinam**
21	8	20	5	29	31	9	21	7	26	62	9	23	10	29	129	8	23	13	40	166	7	24	13	51	195	8	25	14	53	Mbabane	**Swaziland**

Rain mm Average monthly rainfall **Sun hrs** Average daily hours of sunshine **Temp °C** Average daily maximum/minimum temperature
Hum % Average midday humidity ★ Figures not available

Temperature Conversion Scale

°C	-40	-30	-20	-10	0	10	20	30	40	°C
°F	-40	-30	-20	-10	0	10 20 30	40 50 60	70 80 90	100 110	°F

| Country | Location | January | | | | | February | | | | | March | | | | | April | | | | | May | | | | | June | | | | |
		Rain mm	Sun hrs	Temp max	Temp min	Hum %	Rain mm	Sun hrs	Temp max	Temp min	Hum %	Rain mm	Sun hrs	Temp max	Temp min	Hum %	Rain mm	Sun hrs	Temp max	Temp min	Hum %	Rain mm	Sun hrs	Temp max	Temp min	Hum %	Rain mm	Sun hrs	Temp max	Temp min	Hum %
Sweden	Gothenburg	51	2	1	-3	81	34	3	1	-4	76	29	5	4	-2	67	39	7	9	3	59	34	9	16	7	54	54	10	19	12	58
	Stockholm	43	1	-1	-5	83	30	3	-1	-5	77	25	5	3	-4	68	31	7	8	1	60	34	9	14	6	53	45	11	19	11	55
Switzerland	Geneva	63	2	4	-2	78	60	4	6	-1	71	55	5	10	2	62	51	7	15	5	56	68	8	19	9	58	89	9	23	13	58
	Lugano	63	4	6	-2	56	67	5	9	-1	52	99	6	13	3	50	148	6	17	7	50	215	6	21	10	53	198	8	25	14	50
	St Moritz	40	4	-1	-9	57	42	5	0	-8	52	36	5	2	-6	52	45	6	6	-2	50	71	6	10	2	52	89	6	14	5	52
	Zurich	74	2	2	-3	74	69	3	5	-2	65	64	5	10	1	55	76	6	15	4	51	101	7	19	8	52	129	7	23	12	52
Syria	Damascus	43	5	12	2	57	43	6	14	4	53	8	7	18	6	42	13	9	24	9	32	3	10	29	13	26	0	12	33	16	22
Taiwan	Taipei	86	3	19	12	71	135	3	18	12	75	178	3	21	14	69	170	4	25	17	71	231	5	28	21	68	290	6	32	23	68
Tanzania	Dar-es-Salaam	61	8	31	24	69	81	7	32	24	68	115	7	32	23	70	286	5	31	23	75	183	7	30	21	68	31	7	29	19	60
Thailand	Bangkok	8	9	32	20	53	20	8	33	22	55	36	9	34	24	56	58	8	35	25	58	198	8	34	25	64	160	6	33	24	67
	Chiang Mai	0	9	29	13	52	10	9	32	14	44	8	9	34	17	40	36	9	36	22	49	122	8	34	23	60	112	6	32	23	67
	Phuket	35	9	31	23	64	38	10	32	23	63	74	9	33	24	64	127	8	33	25	71	297	7	31	25	74	264	6	31	25	73
Togo	Lomé	15	7	31	22	64	24	8	32	24	66	74	7	32	24	67	107	7	32	24	69	154	7	31	23	73	271	5	30	22	78
Tonga	Nuku'alofa	135	6	29	22	74	191	7	29	23	75	218	5	29	23	77	130	5	28	22	73	140	5	26	20	74	109	5	25	18	74
Trinidad & Tobago	Trinidad	69	7	31	21	68	41	8	31	20	65	46	8	32	20	61	53	8	32	21	63	94	8	32	22	63	193	6	32	22	69
Tunisia	Tunis	79	5	15	7	68	48	6	16	7	64	41	7	18	9	61	41	8	21	11	60	29	10	25	14	53	12	11	29	18	50
Turkey	Ankara	33	3	4	-4	70	31	4	6	-3	67	33	6	11	-1	52	33	7	17	4	40	31	9	23	9	38	25	11	26	12	34
	Istanbul	109	3	8	3	75	92	4	9	2	72	72	4	11	3	67	46	6	16	7	62	38	9	21	12	61	34	11	25	16	58
	Izmir	112	4	13	4	62	84	6	14	4	51	76	6	17	6	52	43	8	21	9	48	33	10	26	13	45	15	12	31	17	40
Turkmenistan	Ashkhabad	25	4	3	-4	69	20	4	8	-1	60	48	5	13	4	54	36	7	21	9	45	31	9	23	16	36	8	11	33	19	29
Turks & Caicos	Grand Turk	56	7	27	21	64	36	8	27	21	62	28	9	28	22	64	38	9	29	23	65	66	9	30	24	65	41	8	31	25	68
Uganda	Kampala	86	5	27	17	63	91	6	27	17	63	179	5	27	18	65	276	4	26	18	70	271	4	25	18	71	107	6	25	17	68
Ukraine	Kiev	58	1	-4	-10	81	59	2	-2	-8	75	51	4	3	-4	69	45	6	14	5	56	49	9	21	11	50	55	9	24	14	51
United Arab Emirates	Abu Dhabi	23	9	23	12	61	23	10	24	14	63	10	9	27	16	61	5	11	30	18	63	0	12	34	22	63	0	12	36	25	65
United Kingdom	Belfast	80	1	6	2	87	52	2	7	2	80	50	3	9	3	74	48	5	12	4	69	52	6	15	6	66	68	6	18	9	71
	Birmingham	74	1	5	2	82	54	2	6	2	76	50	3	9	3	68	53	5	12	5	58	64	5	16	7	58	50	6	19	10	59
	Cardiff	108	2	7	2	89	72	3	7	2	87	63	4	10	3	82	65	5	13	5	74	76	6	16	8	74	63	7	19	11	73
	Edinburgh	57	2	6	1	84	39	3	6	1	83	39	4	8	2	81	39	5	11	4	75	54	6	14	6	76	47	6	17	9	75
	London	54	1	6	2	77	40	2	7	2	72	37	4	10	3	64	37	5	13	6	56	46	6	17	8	57	45	7	20	12	58
	Oban	146	1	6	2	*	109	2	7	1	*	83	3	9	3	*	90	5	11	4	*	72	7	14	7	*	87	6	16	9	*
United States	Anchorage	20	2	-6	-15	74	18	3	-3	-12	66	13	6	1	-10	58	11	9	7	-3	52	13	8	13	3	50	25	10	17	7	56
	Atlanta	112	5	12	2	62	84	6	13	3	58	137	6	17	5	54	114	8	22	10	49	81	9	27	15	50	97	10	31	20	52
	Boston	99	5	3	-5	60	84	6	3	-5	58	107	7	7	-1	55	97	7	13	4	54	84	9	20	10	55	89	10	25	15	57
	Chicago	47	4	1	-7	70	41	5	2	-6	67	70	6	6	-2	61	77	7	14	5	55	95	9	21	11	55	103	10	26	16	56
	Columbus	81	3	3	-4	71	58	4	5	-4	67	81	6	9	0	60	89	7	16	6	55	102	8	23	12	54	107	10	28	17	53
	Dallas	58	5	13	2	62	74	7	15	4	61	74	7	19	7	54	102	8	24	13	54	122	9	28	17	56	81	11	33	22	53
	Honolulu	97	7	26	19	64	84	8	26	19	62	74	9	26	19	60	33	9	27	20	59	25	10	28	21	58	8	10	29	22	58
	Kansas City	36	4	4	-5	64	30	6	7	-3	60	63	6	11	1	56	91	8	19	8	51	112	9	24	13	53	117	11	30	19	54
	Las Vegas	13	8	12	0	40	10	9	15	2	33	8	10	20	6	25	5	11	25	11	20	3	12	31	15	16	0	14	36	20	13
	Los Angeles	69	7	18	7	49	74	8	18	8	51	46	9	18	9	50	28	9	19	11	54	3	9	20	13	56	3	10	22	15	60
	Miami	51	8	24	14	59	48	8	25	15	56	58	9	27	16	56	99	9	28	19	56	163	9	30	21	59	188	9	31	23	64
	New Orleans	97	5	18	7	65	102	6	19	9	62	135	7	22	11	58	114	8	25	15	58	112	9	28	18	58	112	9	32	21	60
	New York	89	5	4	-3	61	74	6	4	-2	58	104	7	9	1	56	89	7	15	6	55	91	8	21	12	56	86	10	26	17	58
	Philadelphia	82	5	5	-3	61	74	6	6	-3	57	96	7	10	1	53	87	8	17	6	49	91	8	23	12	51	99	10	28	17	53
	Phoenix	18	8	18	2	44	23	10	20	4	42	18	11	24	6	31	8	12	29	10	25	3	13	34	14	19	3	14	39	19	17
	San Francisco	102	5	13	5	75	89	7	15	6	71	69	8	16	7	66	33	10	18	8	66	13	11	19	10	66	3	11	21	11	65
	Seattle	139	2	8	2	78	107	4	9	3	75	90	5	12	4	69	55	7	15	6	61	40	8	19	9	60	36	8	21	11	61
	Washington	84	5	7	-1	58	68	6	8	0	56	96	7	12	2	49	85	8	19	8	46	103	9	25	13	51	88	9	29	18	52
Uruguay	Montevideo	74	11	28	17	53	66	10	28	16	55	99	9	26	15	57	99	8	22	12	61	80	6	18	9	66	81	5	15	6	69
Uzbekistan	Tashkent	53	4	3	-6	63	28	4	7	-3	58	66	5	12	3	55	58	8	18	8	52	36	10	26	13	42	13	12	31	17	34
Vanuatu	Port-Vila	259	6	31	23	73	285	7	31	24	75	297	6	30	23	76	244	5	29	23	79	142	6	27	22	76	125	6	27	21	76
Venezuela	Caracas	23	8	24	13	66	10	9	25	13	63	15	8	26	14	63	33	7	27	16	67	79	6	27	17	67	102	7	26	17	67
Vietnam	Hanoi	18	1	20	13	68	28	1	21	14	70	38	1	23	17	76	81	2	28	20	75	196	4	32	23	69	239	5	33	26	71
	Ho Chi Minh City	15	5	32	21	61	3	6	33	22	56	13	5	34	23	58	43	6	35	24	60	221	4	33	24	71	330	4	32	24	78
Virgin Islands	Tortola	104	8	29	22	69	51	8	29	22	66	58	10	30	23	65	58	9	31	23	67	97	9	32	24	71	91	8	32	24	71
Western Samoa	Apia	455	6	30	24	79	386	6	29	24	78	358	6	30	23	78	254	6	30	24	76	160	7	29	23	76	130	7	29	23	73
Yemen	Aden	5	11	28	22	63	0	10	28	23	65	5	9	30	24	66	0	10	32	25	66	0	9	34	27	66	0	10	37	29	51
Yugoslavia	Belgrade	47	2	3	-3	75	46	3	5	-2	67	46	5	11	2	56	54	6	18	7	49	74	7	23	12	51	96	9	26	15	51
Zaire (Dem Rep of Congo)	Kinshasa	128	4	31	22	71	142	5	31	22	70	173	5	32	22	68	222	5	32	22	68	129	5	31	22	71	4	4	28	19	69
Zambia	Lusaka	224	5	26	17	64	173	5	26	17	65	90	7	26	16	56	19	9	27	15	47	3	9	25	12	38	1	9	23	10	36
Zimbabwe	Bulawayo	127	7	27	17	45	109	8	27	16	49	68	8	26	15	43	32	9	26	13	40	10	9	23	10	33	2	10	21	7	33
	Harare	178	6	26	16	57	158	7	26	16	58	85	7	26	14	49	39	9	26	13	44	10	9	23	9	37	5	9	21	7	37
	Victoria Falls	181	6	29	19	55	165	6	29	19	56	88	8	30	18	44	23	9	30	15	36	2	10	28	10	28	2	10	25	7	28

Rain mm Average monthly rainfall   **Sun hrs** Average daily hours of sunshine   **Temp °C** Average daily maximum/minimum temperature
Hum % Average midday humidity   * Figures not available

Rainfall Conversion Scale

mm	5	25	50	75	100	150	200	300	600	1200
in	0.2	1	2	3	4	6	8	12	24	48

Weather Statistics

July Rain mm	July Sun hrs	July Temp °C max	July min	July Hum %	Aug Rain mm	Aug Sun hrs	Aug Temp °C max	Aug min	Aug Hum %	Sep Rain mm	Sep Sun hrs	Sep Temp °C max	Sep min	Sep Hum %	Oct Rain mm	Oct Sun hrs	Oct Temp °C max	Oct min	Oct Hum %	Nov Rain mm	Nov Sun hrs	Nov Temp °C max	Nov min	Nov Hum %	Dec Rain mm	Dec Sun hrs	Dec Temp °C max	Dec min	Dec Hum %	Location	Country
86	9	21	14	62	84	8	20	13	63	75	6	16	10	67	65	3	11	6	72	62	2	6	3	80	57	1	4	0	83	Gothenburg	Sweden
61	10	22	14	59	76	8	20	13	64	60	6	15	9	69	48	3	9	5	76	53	1	5	1	85	48	1	2	-2	86	Stockholm	
64	10	25	15	56	94	9	24	14	59	99	7	21	12	65	72	4	14	7	71	83	2	8	3	76	59	1	4	0	79	Geneva	Switzerland
185	9	27	16	48	196	8	27	15	51	159	6	23	13	54	173	5	16	8	57	147	4	11	3	59	95	3	7	0	59	Lugano	
105	7	15	7	51	101	6	15	7	53	83	6	13	5	54	77	5	9	1	55	67	3	4	-4	59	48	3	0	-7	60	St Moritz	
136	8	25	14	52	124	7	24	13	53	102	6	20	11	57	77	3	14	6	64	73	2	7	2	73	64	1	3	-2	76	Zurich	
0	13	36	18	19	0	12	37	18	21	18	10	33	16	24	10	8	27	12	31	41	7	19	8	46	41	5	13	4	59	Damascus	Syria
231	7	33	24	62	305	7	33	24	64	244	6	31	23	66	122	5	27	19	65	66	3	24	17	65	71	3	21	14	69	Taipei	Taiwan
29	7	29	19	58	26	9	29	18	57	32	9	30	19	58	62	9	30	20	61	104	8	31	22	66	95	8	31	23	69	Dar-es-Salaam	Tanzania
160	5	32	24	66	175	5	32	24	66	305	5	32	24	70	206	6	31	24	70	66	8	31	22	65	5	9	31	20	56	Bangkok	Thailand
213	5	31	23	69	193	4	31	23	73	249	6	31	23	72	94	7	31	21	69	31	8	30	19	63	13	9	28	15	57	Chiang Mai	
216	6	31	25	73	244	6	31	24	74	328	5	30	24	77	315	6	31	24	77	193	7	31	24	73	79	8	31	24	68	Phuket	
93	4	28	22	78	25	4	28	22	75	43	5	29	22	74	111	7	29	22	72	25	8	31	23	68	7	8	31	23	63	Lomé	Togo
109	5	25	18	71	137	5	24	18	72	112	5	25	18	72	99	7	26	19	71	104	7	27	21	70	127	8	28	21	72	Nuku'alofa	Tonga
218	7	31	22	71	246	7	31	22	73	193	7	32	22	73	170	7	32	22	74	183	7	32	22	76	125	7	31	21	71	Trinidad	Trinidad & Tobago
2	12	32	20	45	14	11	32	21	48	26	9	29	20	54	85	7	25	16	59	56	6	21	12	63	47	5	16	9	67	Tunis	Tunisia
13	12	30	15	28	10	12	31	15	25	18	10	26	11	31	23	7	21	7	37	31	5	14	3	52	48	3	6	-2	71	Ankara	Turkey
34	12	28	18	56	30	11	28	19	55	58	8	24	16	59	81	6	20	13	64	103	4	15	9	71	119	3	11	5	74	Istanbul	
5	13	33	21	31	5	12	33	21	37	20	10	29	17	42	53	8	24	13	49	84	6	19	9	58	122	4	14	6	64	Izmir	
3	12	36	22	28	3	11	35	19	27	3	10	30	14	30	13	8	22	8	39	20	5	14	3	57	18	4	8	0	65	Ashkhabad	Turkmenistan
43	9	32	25	69	51	9	32	26	70	81	7	31	25	73	102	7	31	24	71	114	7	29	23	68	69	7	28	22	66	Grand Turk	Turks & Caicos
68	6	25	16	67	84	5	25	16	68	78	5	26	17	66	108	5	26	17	65	158	5	26	17	65	121	4	26	17	65	Kampala	Uganda
91	10	25	15	53	91	8	24	14	55	30	7	20	10	54	33	5	13	6	65	56	2	6	0	82	59	1	-1	-6	84	Kiev	Ukraine
0	9	38	28	64	0	10	39	28	64	0	11	37	25	64	0	10	33	22	62	10	10	31	18	59	36	9	26	14	62	Abu Dhabi	United Arab Emirates
94	4	18	11	73	77	4	18	11	75	80	4	16	9	78	83	3	13	7	79	72	3	9	4	85	90	1	7	3	89	Belfast	United Kingdom
69	5	20	12	62	69	5	20	12	64	61	4	17	10	67	69	3	13	7	73	84	2	9	5	80	67	1	6	3	84	Birmingham	
89	6	20	12	76	97	6	21	13	78	99	5	18	11	81	109	3	14	8	85	116	2	10	5	88	108	2	8	3	89	Cardiff	
83	5	18	11	77	77	4	18	11	80	57	4	16	9	80	65	3	12	7	82	62	2	9	4	83	57	1	7	2	84	Edinburgh	
57	6	22	14	59	59	6	21	13	62	49	5	19	11	65	57	3	14	8	70	64	2	10	5	78	48	1	7	4	81	London	
120	4	17	11	*	116	4	17	11	*	141	4	15	9	*	169	2	12	7	*	146	1	9	4	*	172	1	7	3	*	Oban	
47	8	19	10	62	65	6	18	9	64	63	4	13	4	65	47	3	6	-2	67	26	2	-2	-9	74	24	2	-7	-14	77	Anchorage	United States
119	9	31	21	57	91	9	31	20	56	84	8	28	17	56	61	7	23	11	52	76	6	17	5	53	112	5	12	2	61	Atlanta	
74	11	28	19	56	94	9	27	17	57	89	8	23	14	59	79	7	17	8	56	99	5	11	3	58	91	5	5	-3	57	Boston	
86	10	29	20	53	80	9	28	19	55	69	8	24	14	53	71	7	17	8	54	56	5	8	0	62	48	4	2	-5	69	Chicago	
99	10	30	19	51	74	10	29	18	52	69	9	25	14	51	53	7	19	8	53	63	5	10	2	62	58	3	5	-3	70	Columbus	
48	11	35	24	50	48	10	35	24	48	71	9	31	20	50	69	8	26	14	51	69	7	19	7	54	69	6	14	3	60	Dallas	
10	11	29	23	58	23	11	29	23	59	25	9	30	23	57	46	8	29	22	66	56	6	28	21	62	76	7	26	20	63	Honolulu	
81	11	33	22	49	97	10	32	21	51	84	9	28	16	49	74	8	22	9	49	46	6	13	1	54	38	5	7	-2	63	Kansas City	
13	12	40	24	18	13	12	38	23	21	8	12	35	19	18	5	10	27	12	24	8	9	18	4	30	10	10	13	1	38	Las Vegas	
1	12	24	17	57	1	11	24	17	57	5	10	24	16	55	10	9	23	14	51	28	8	22	11	42	61	8	19	9	47	Los Angeles	
170	9	32	24	64	178	8	32	24	63	241	7	31	24	66	208	6	29	22	64	71	7	27	18	60	43	7	25	15	60	Miami	
170	8	33	23	65	135	8	33	23	64	127	8	31	21	63	71	8	27	16	57	84	6	21	10	58	104	5	19	8	65	New Orleans	
102	10	28	20	57	119	9	27	19	60	89	8	24	16	60	84	7	18	10	59	89	5	12	4	60	84	5	6	-1	60	New York	
98	10	30	20	53	109	8	29	19	55	79	8	25	15	55	71	7	20	9	53	86	5	13	3	56	76	5	6	-2	59	Philadelphia	
20	13	40	24	29	28	12	39	23	35	18	12	37	20	29	13	10	30	13	30	23	9	23	6	33	23	9	19	3	42	Phoenix	
1	10	22	12	69	1	9	22	12	69	5	9	23	12	66	18	8	21	10	65	41	7	18	8	68	104	6	14	6	74	San Francisco	
17	10	24	13	61	19	8	24	13	67	46	7	21	11	70	88	4	16	8	77	137	3	11	5	80	145	2	9	3	81	Seattle	
108	9	31	21	53	120	8	30	20	55	100	8	26	16	55	78	7	20	10	54	75	5	14	4	52	75	4	8	-1	55	Washington	
74	5	14	6	69	79	6	15	6	67	76	7	17	8	65	66	7	19	10	64	74	10	23	12	56	79	10	26	15	52	Montevideo	Uruguay
5	13	38	18	33	3	12	36	16	32	3	10	27	11	34	31	8	15	8	43	38	5	12	2	55	41	4	7	-2	62	Tashkent	Uzbekistan
97	7	26	19	73	89	6	26	19	72	97	7	27	20	70	122	7	28	21	70	168	8	29	22	69	180	7	31	23	70	Port-Vila	Vanuatu
109	8	26	16	67	109	8	26	16	60	107	7	27	16	57	109	7	26	16	64	94	7	25	16	68	46	7	26	14	66	Caracas	Venezuela
323	5	33	26	72	343	4	32	26	75	254	4	31	24	73	99	4	29	22	69	43	3	26	18	68	20	2	22	15	67	Hanoi	Vietnam
315	4	31	24	80	269	5	31	24	78	335	5	31	23	80	269	4	31	23	80	114	4	31	23	75	56	4	31	22	68	Ho Chi Minh City	
112	9	31	23	71	132	9	32	24	72	152	7	32	24	73	137	8	32	24	73	183	7	31	24	74	114	7	29	22	72	Tortola	Virgin Islands
81	7	29	23	75	89	7	29	24	73	132	8	29	23	75	170	6	29	24	76	267	6	30	23	75	371	6	29	23	77	Apia	Western Samoa
5	7	36	28	56	3	6	38	28	56	0	10	36	28	58	0	11	33	24	58	0	10	30	23	61	5	10	28	23	62	Aden	Yemen
61	10	28	17	47	55	9	28	17	46	50	8	24	13	47	55	3	18	8	52	61	3	11	4	71	55	2	5	0	76	Belgrade	Yugoslavia
3	4	27	17	66	3	5	29	18	61	46	4	30	20	61	145	5	31	21	65	246	5	31	21	70	161	4	30	22	71	Kinshasa (Dem Rep of Congo)	Zaire
1	9	23	9	34	1	10	26	11	29	1	9	29	15	25	17	9	31	18	26	85	7	29	18	44	196	6	27	17	60	Lusaka	Zambia
1	9	21	7	30	2	10	24	9	27	1	10	27	12	23	33	9	30	16	27	84	7	28	16	41	123	8	27	16	46	Bulawayo	Zimbabwe
1	9	21	7	36	3	10	24	8	30	1	10	27	11	.26	31	10	28	15	30	97	7	27	15	44	169	7	26	16	56	Harare	
0	10	26	7	26	1	10	28	10	22	2	10	32	15	18	25	9	35	19	21	82	7	32	19	37	172	6	30	19	52	Victoria Falls	

Rain mm Average monthly rainfall **Sun hrs** Average daily hours of sunshine **Temp °C** Average daily maximum/minimum temperature
Hum % Average midday humidity ∗ Figures not available

°C	-40	-30	-20	-10	0	10	20	30	40	°C
°F	-40	-30	-20	-10	0	10	20	30	40	50	60	70	80	90	100	110	°F

Temperature Conversion Scale

A glossary of Wind names and other terms referred to within the weather descriptions on pages 8 - 91. Climatic types are described on page 7.

Berg Wind A wind which blows from the mountains in the interior down to the southern and western coasts of South Africa and Namibia. It blows during the winter season and brings warmer temperatures than is usual for that time of year.

Bora A cold blustery wind which blows mainly in winter and spring on the northern Adriatic coast and the north Italian plain.

Buran A bitterly cold wind which blows in Siberian Russia in the winter and spring and is associated with blizzard conditions.

Chinook A föhn type of wind which blows on the eastern side of the Rockies in Canada and the United States. It is particularly noted for its warmth and dryness which melts lying snow rapidly in spring.

Cyclone A general term for a type of tropical weather disturbance in the Indian Ocean where strong winds circulating round a centre of low pressure cause heavy cloud and rain. Cyclones go under various other local names such as Hurricane in the North Atlantic, Typhoon in the western Pacific and China Sea.

Etesion Wind A constant north to northwesterly wind which blows in the eastern Mediterranean and the Aegean from early June to mid-September, generally a season of fine and settled weather.

Föhn A relatively warm, dry wind with no humidity which blows in the Alps in spring and can melt snow very rapidly.

Ghibli A hot dry wind which blows from the Sahara Desert, particularly in the spring, towards the Mediterranean coast of northwest Africa and produces unusually hot but normally settled weather, with dust and sand storms.

Guinea Monsoon The summer rains which occur on the southward facing coasts of West Africa when the northeast trade winds disappear for three or four months and are replaced by warm and humid winds from the South Atlantic.

Haboob A short relatively violent weather disturbance in central Sudan which brings strong, gusty winds and often a dust storm. It is associated with a change from the predominate southwesterly to easterly wind direction.

Harmattan The term given to the dry northeasterly trade winds often associated with dust or even sand storms which prevail in the winter period in West Africa on the area inland from the Guinea Coast. It is the opposite, in a sense, of the Guinea Monsoon.

High Sun The opposite of Low Sun, and refers to the period in the tropics when the sun is at its maximum midday altitude in that particular hemisphere. The rainy season in much of the tropics is associated with the period of High Sun, the dry season with the period of Low Sun, and these are more appropriate terms for the tropics than winter and summer.

Hurricane The name given to tropical cyclones in the North Atlantic, the Caribbean and the southeastern United States. Hurricanes tend to occur during the months of July to October, the period known as the hurricane season.

Khamsin An Arabic name for a hot dry and often dust laden wind blowing in the spring and autumn from the interior which produces high temperatures on the Mediterranean coasts of Egypt, Israel (where it is known as Sharav) Lebanon and Syria.

Land and Sea Breezes A local wind system which occurs during fine and settled weather on the coast in the tropics, on tropical islands and, for example, in the Mediterranean. A light wind that blows from the sea during the day and from the land at night.

Leveche The name given in Southern Spain for a dry wind which originates in the Sahara and brings hot and humid conditions.

Low Sun The opposite of High Sun and refers to the period in the tropics when the sun is at its minimum midday altitude in that hemisphere.

Mistral A strong wind which may persist for several days and is peculiar to southern France, particularly the Rhône valley. In winter and spring it brings cold air and in summer it can fan forest fires.

Monsoon Rains The name given in India and southeast Asia to the normally heavy rains of the wet season. The term is also used in East Africa and West Africa (The Guinea Monsoon).

Monsoon Winds The seasonal prevailing winds which alternate between the dry northeast land monsoon and the wet southwest ocean monsoon of the Indian sub-continent.

Mountain and Valley Winds Similar to Land and Sea Breezes, these are light winds which blow in fine and settled weather to the centre of mountain ranges during the day and then outwards down the valleys at night.

Shamal The Arabic name for a northwesterly wind which blows during the hot summer season in central and southern Iraq, and the Persian Gulf.

Sirocco A warm southerly wind from the Sahara which picks up moisture over the Mediterranean sea and brings warm and humid conditions to its northern shores, particularly of Italy and Greece in the autumn.

Sukhovey A Russian name for a dry, desiccating wind which may blow, on occasions, in the steppes of southern Russia.

Tornado A name given in the United States to a violent whirlwind associated with thunder cloud which may cause extensive damage along its narrow track.

Trade Winds The term for the constant winds which occur over most oceans within the tropics and blow inwards towards the equator.

Typhoon The name given in the Western Pacific and China Sea to a violent type of tropical disturbance similar to Hurricanes and Cyclones, bringing very strong winds and heavy rainfall.

Willy Willies An Australian term for violent tropical storms affecting the coasts of Northern Australia.

Wind Chill The term for the cooling effect of the wind: a brisk wind in hot climates helps keep one cool, but in cold climates makes one feel even colder. Where very low temperatures and strong winds are normal in the winter, the cooling power of the wind is rated by a Wind Chill Index.